Dear Karla
thank you for June E Busson

Skinny Scotty

*"I just finished reading a manuscript copy of **Skinny Scotty**. I expected it to be a biographical work, of course, but I was especially delighted to find that it was such a charmingly intimate story about what life was really like for ordinary people in the early 1900s. I'm sure readers can expect to shed a few tears of sadness and a few tears of joy. I know I did."*

—Philip Leslie, retired Registrar of the Smithsonian Institution

Skinny Scotty

The Adventurous Life of Rosa Ellen Scott

JUNE ELIZABETH BUSSARD

BOOKS

Published by J&J Books
664 A Freeman Lane #426
Grass Valley, CA 95949

ISBN #0-9652014-0-6

LCCN / CIP #96-94290

Cover design: Joseph M. Bussard

Painting of lady on horseback, "Helping Hand," by William Dunton,
used by permission of Rockwell Museum in Corning, New York.

Printed in the United States of America
by Blue Dolphin Press, Grass Valley, California

5   4   3   2   1

Dedication

For MOTHER and DAD

Table of Contents

Foreword

Rosa Ellen Scott is my mother; I am her second daughter, June Elizabeth.

Rosa was born in 1895 in Magley, Indiana; she lived ninety-four and one-half years. This is the true story of her early life, told in her own words, with her own unpolished language, just as she spoke.

During the first nine years of Rosa's life, she was taunted with the contemptuous nickname, "Skinny Scotty, the Rebel Brat." This scornful taunt colored her whole life. Somehow though, it made her strong, self-reliant, and very feisty.

When we children were growing up, Mother told us some of the stories of her childhood, but in her later years she seemed to take great pleasure remembering and recounting these fascinating tales in great detail. I spent many days with her when she was in her nineties and blind. I loved to hear her stories, and I am so glad I tape-recorded our many conversations together. Those tapes eventually became this book.

Skinny Scotty's life is, almost word for word, just as she related her tales to me. I promised Mother many times, "Someday, I will write a book about your life, about Skinny Scotty." She would always laugh and say, "Oh little sweetheart, that would be nice for the grandchildren; maybe that would help them understand what it was like living in those days. But don't you tell everything!"

For many years after her death I was dealing with a great burden of grief and could not bring myself to listen to her voice. But after a wonderful change occurred in my life, I felt contentment again, and I was able to keep my promise to her.

From the very beginning of this writing I felt a great joy and a complete fascination with her extraordinary life, especially her young years. Of course there is also the tender love story between my handsome, dynamic father and Rosa Ellen. His life too was very unique. He was a determined, competent young man, fighting for his own beliefs, even if it meant losing his own life.

It was not easy transcribing Mother's tales into a story, as I am not a writer. But her sincere words were there speaking to me, and I put them down on paper. However, just words do not make a very readable book. I had the help of a fine editor. Mr. Steve Koke not only did a remarkable job of editing, but had infinite patience and intuitive suggestions. It was certainly a pleasure and an education for me to work with Mr. Koke.

That wonderful change which came into my life was marrying an exceptional man a few years ago, Mr. Joe Bussard. His heartfelt understanding and loving support made it possible for me to spend the many hours, actually the two years, needed to complete Mother's story. And again I was blessed to add five more adult children to my family, and five more grandchildren. I am also thankful to Joe's youngest son, Joseph M. Bussard. Joseph used his graphic design talents to artistically design this beautiful cover for Mother's book. Like Rosa, I have been a very, very lucky woman.

Writing this has been a joyous experience for me. Skinny Scotty and I hope you will enjoy her story.

June Elizabeth

Skinny Scotty

CHAPTER ONE

ℳagley, Indiana 1899

LITTLE ROSA SNUGGLED DOWN deeper into the softness of the feather mattress. She felt the welcome warmth of her sister Louisa. "Oh," Rosa moaned to herself, "feet cold, so cold, all icicle toes." She tried to scrunch her long flannel gown around her skinny legs. Her tears against the cotton ticking made her cheeks numb with cold. She sobbed and sniffled and felt all sick in her middle. Tomorrow was to be her number four birthday. But now, she would not be having the wild plum puddin' that her mama always made for birthdays. She would not be the birthday girl all day, with her brothers and sisters clapping and singing just for her. It would not be her special day at all.

Mama had told her that Papa had "gone to heaven," and tomorrow was the day they must "take him out to rest." So now, there would be no singing for Rosa's birthday, no plum puddin' with molasses syrup on top, no nuthin' at all.

Her older sister Belle was softly moving the covers so that she could get into the bed. Now, Rosa's back would be warm. Belle was larger and rounder and softer than all her sisters and always warmer. Belle patted Rosa's little shaking shoulders and made those shush-shush sing-songs like she did when Rosa was a little bitty baby. Oh yes, she still did cry a lot, but sister Belle always made everything all right again.

This was the night of October 28th in the year 1899. The winter was miserably cold, and there was that icy wind that always howled through the little town of Magley, Indiana. Rosa was turning four years old tomorrow, the youngest of ten children born to Mary Catherine Scott and James Henry Scott. Papa Scott had fought in the Civil War, but no one ever knew whether he fought for the North or for the South. However, he was a tall, skinny, slow-moving man, with a gentle southern accent and a fair education, so therefore there were a great many questions about his background and just where his loyalties lay.

Rosa's mama never told anyone who papa Scott fought for in the War. Maybe she didn't even know herself, but somehow he was branded a "Rebel" by the good folks of Indiana. He was never very well; everyone said he developed a lung disease from being in the prison camps.

Rosa's memories of her father were very sketchy. In later years, she often said of Papa Scott, "Oh, he was only good at makin' babies, but Mama loved him dearly, so I guess that's all that counts." Then she would say, "One time, when I was very little, I remember looking up at him when he came through the kitchen door. He was singing "Yankee Doodle" and banging on a pan with Mama's spoon. He was so silly he made us all laugh right out loud."

In that early morning of Rosa's fourth birthday on October 29, 1899, a drizzle of rain and snow was falling on the small wooden frame house of the Scotts. Rosa was standing out on the front porch, and, oh my, she was awful cold again. Her mama had told her to stay out there and to not come in till she saw the big wagon coming. It was a very, very important chore to do for her mama, so she kept her eyes glued to the roadway. It was misty, but maybe, if she listened real hard, she might hear the wagon crunching along on the frozen road.

She kept stomping her feet up and down in her too-large shoes. They were sister Belle's hightop buttonup ones, but Belle had tied a heavy cord around the tops for Rosa, so they stayed on pretty good and could not fall off Rosa's tiny feet. The tears were freezing her cheeks, so she angrily wiped them away with her sleeve. Her number four birthday— today was her number four birthday. She moved her fingers in her sweater pocket, 1-2-3-4. Her number four birthday, and no singing, no clapping, no special puddin', just "take Papa to rest." She had touched the big box in the house where they had put Papa. The boards were rough and heavy. She wondered if the box would keep her papa warm and dry. Oh, she hoped it would; it was so cold today.

Rosa had asked each one of her brothers and sisters, and Mama too, "Will Papa stay warm in the big box?" But no one wanted to even talk to her. "Not now, little sister, I must do what Mama told me to do. Not now, Rosa. Don't ask so many questions, Rosa Ellen." And then Mama had told her, "Just go outside and be on watch for the wagon, Rosa." So, she must listen real good.

There, maybe she heard crunching. And yes, hooves stomping. My, now the stomping sounded louder, but she could not see anything through the mist and falling snow.

And then, suddenly, there, right there by the gate, right there, were two large black horses, stomping their heavy legs up and down as if they were angry. Big tassels wobbled on the heavy heads, and behind them was a huge, black wagon. Rosa jumped back in sudden fear and fell over Mama's rocker and hurt her arm. Her little heart thumped so fast. The horses and the big black wagon were very scary.

She jerked open the door, crying and sobbing, "Mama, Mama, the horses, the horses." Again sister Belle held her close and shushed her. "Now, now, Rosa, don't be a scaredy-cat; those are just nice, friendly horses. You see, we must put Papa's box in the wagon and take him to rest. It will be all right, Rosa Ellen; now go on out and look at those nice horses. We will all be leaving in a minute."

The big driver was bundled up in a slicker coat, standing in front of his team, holding the horses. He called to her and showed her that the horses were really very gentle. "They will not hurt little girls," he told her, "as long as you don't run right under them. See, I'll hold you up, and you can pet old Abraham on his white nose. There, see, he likes you."

Rosa patted the warm nose, and it felt all soft and smooth. Oh, how she wanted to reach up and touch that big, black tassel sticking up from the huge head, but maybe that would be too high up for the driver to lift her. The horse's muzzle was soft and steaming, and her hand felt so warm there. Oh, she wished she could just keep it there on the velvety warmth for a long, long time.

When the driver asked her mama if Rosa could ride up top with him while he drove the horses, she wanted to do that so bad that she held her breath till it hurt, as she waited for her mama's decision. Her mama finally said it would be all right and to ask brother Scott to let Rosa wear his heavy coat and hat.

The driver lifted her up onto the high wooden seat. "Oh," Rosa sighed, "I never been so high up before; well, the apple tree is high, but it don't move." The big man smiled at her and told her to hold on as tight as she could. The horses started stomping along and tossing their big heads up and down. The driver held them tight, with his hands wrapped in the leather reins. His boot was braced against the wagon panel. Oh, the steam rising from the two big bodies of the horses smelled so good.

Rosa had been told that Mama and her brothers and sisters were coming along behind in the funny-looking buckboard. She had wanted to look inside that one because it had a fancy top, but there was not time, and Belle had told Rosa that she would be riding home in that one anyway.

She swallowed real hard. Here she was, all alone with the driver, way up on this big wagon. She was so excited she didn't feel the icy wind or her feet turning numb. The driver even let her put her hands on the reins to feel the mighty pull of the horses. Oh my, oh my, she thought, I love these big, black horses, and I know that ol' Abraham will be my friend forever and ever and ever.

Later on that same day, Rosa stood out on their front porch again, thinking out loud, "This is just ezzactly what Mama told me to do this morning, and here I am again, out on the porch on watch." Mama had told her, in kind of a cross voice for Mama, "Rosa, please just go out on the porch steps and wait. Be a good girl now, and say a polite welcome to anyone coming up the path."

Well, Rosa didn't see anyone at all, and it was cold out here. But anyway, she still felt all good inside when she thought about the big, friendly Abraham-horse. She promised herself over and over, "Someday I will have a big, black horse like ol' Abraham, someday for sure."

It was still windy, but it had stopped snowing. Rosa stomped her cold feet again and again. Then she was startled to see a tall lady wearing a black hat coming through their gate. The lady was carrying something in the crook of her arm.

Rosa's "Welcome, welcome, Ma'am" was almost out before she saw the scowling face and the beady eyes glaring at her. Rosa remembered this lady from church. She was one of the ladies that always sat up front and always dressed different than her mama. Rosa was a little scared and blurted out, "Are you bringing us something to eat in that bowl?"

"Yes," the lady said, "it's a dish for the family." And then she added, almost under her breath, "You skinny little Rebel brat."

Rosa knew what the "Rebel brat" meant because she had heard that many times before. The mean children in the town always called her "Skinny Scotty, the Rebel brat," and it always made her feel so very bad. She burst into tears and quickly ran around to the back of the house and leaned against the shed and cried and cried. No birthday for Rosa Ellen, no clapping, no singing, just take Papa to rest, and now this hateful ol' lady calling her names. Well, she would tell her sisters what the lady had called her, and she wouldn't even taste what was in that ol' bowl.

Two mornings later, after eating her mush, Rosa was supposed to sit quietly with her brothers and sisters and just wait. Just wait, because they were going to have callers.

Soon the visitors arrived. It was the preacher and his wife and another lady. The preacher was a short, pudgy man. His red face and snow-white whiskers always looked funny to Rosa, but she didn't feel like smiling today. She did manage a little smile for the preacher's wife because Rosa really liked her. The lady always seemed so soft and fluttery that she reminded Rosa of a pretty spring butterfly.

"Oh no," Rosa moaned. "The other lady is that hateful lady that called me a skinny Rebel brat." Rosa squirmed in her chair and looked down at her shoes. Well, anyway, she had only tasted a couple of spoons of that ol' potato and sausage dish. She didn't eat very much of it.

The preacher was talking and talking in his big, deep voice. He was telling her mama, "It is for the best, Mrs. Scott, for the children, and they will have good homes and be able to go to school regularly." He was going on and on, and Rosa just didn't understand what he was talking about. They already had a good home, and her older brothers and sisters attended school when they could. Sometimes Mama and Papa could not give them too much for supper, but sometimes there was even plum pudding with sweet molasses glaze on the top. Big tears rolled down Rosa's cheeks when she thought about the lost birthday. It would be such a very long time before her number five birthday.

Suddenly Mama stood up and stomped her foot. "No," she shouted, "No, never, never, never! I will not give up any one of my children. We will stay together; we will make-do; we will make-do together." She walked hurriedly over to the door, swung it open quickly and stood beside it as if she was all done with the talkin'.

The preacher picked up his hat and walked quickly out with that mean ol' lady behind him. The preacher's wife looked sad and put her arm around Mama's shoulders for a moment, and then she also hurried out. Mama slammed the door behind them and sat down in her rocking chair and started to cry. Louisa scurried to get Mama some sassafras tea. Belle knelt down beside Mama and held her in her arms and made her shushing sing-songs, just like she did for Rosa when Rosa felt bad.

In two months it was Christmas, and the family was not all together. The older children, Clarissa, David, William, Phylie and Henry, were all out doing domestic work. They were working with different families for their keep and could not get any time off to come home. So there would only be Belle who was 11, Bert who was 9, Louisa who was 7, Rosa, now 4 years old, and Mama, still at home. But some green boughs were cut and brought in the house, and Mama's silver tea set was on the table. Mama's tea set was special. It was very pretty, and Rosa knew how to polish it all by herself. Rosa loved to walk into the room and see it on the table. It made the house look so happy. There was the warm stove; there were presents of colorful, knitted woolen mufflers for all. There was even a big plum puddin'.

Rosa knew this Christmas was going to be very lonely for her mama. The sisters and brothers did what they could to make it a nicer time for her. In the evenings Rosa would coax Mama to sing carols. "Oh Mama," she told her, "come sing with us. You know I can't sing very good, can't even carry the tune in a basket, but I love to sing, and you sing so nice. Come, sing with us." And her mama smiled and sang along with all of them.

During that long winter, Mama continued to do washin's out in the lean-to shed behind the house every day. She would bring home huge baskets of laundry from people in town, or someone would drop them off on their porch. This was what Mama had to do to be able to pay for things, and she was very good at it. She had been doing this for a long time.

Mama had two big tin tubs on a wooden stand with a wringer in the middle. There was a large iron pot held with a hook on a swinging arm that could swing the big pot over the open fire pit. The fire was Bert and Rosa's chore. They must make sure there was firewood to keep the coals hot most of the morning. The hot fire in the pit also helped dry the clothes hanging on lines inside the shed. Mama would move her big plunger up and down on the clothes in the wash tubs, which was very hard work. The girls would help her by turning the wringer that wrung most of the water out of the clothes. After the clothes were hung and finally dry, Mama would bring the big basket into the kitchen and iron 'most every evening. Her heavy black irons were kept very hot on top of the cook stove. Mama had a wooden handle that would just snap onto the next hot iron. The work was very, very hard, and Mama grew awful thin and tired looking. Rosa and the other children helped out as best they could, and they all took turns sawing wood for fuel. But Mama insisted that the three older ones go to school every day that it was not too cold.

"Next year," Mama told Rosa, "you will go to school with your sisters." Even though she was not quite old enough for the first grade, she would be able to go. Rosa was very excited about starting school and asked Belle and Louisa over and over to tell her what school would be like.

Finally, next school year arrived, and Rosa trudged to school with her sisters. Mama had made "special arrangements" with the schoolmarm. Rosa could sit in the back of the classroom, but only if she would be very quiet during the time the children were learning their lessons. Rosa knew why her Mama had planned this. It was because Mama could then go out to other people's homes to do work like cannin' and butcherin' and washin', places where she could not take a little girl with her.

Oh, Rosa loved to go to school. So she was very happy just to sit and listen. The teacher even told stories. But sometimes Rosa would get kind of fidgety because she had to sit extra quiet while the students did numbers on their slates. She loved to look at the little book the teacher laid out for her, but in a short time she learned all the pictures by heart. She wanted to ask the teacher to give her another book, one with words in it, but was afraid that might be too forward for a little girl who was not even supposed to be in school yet.

Two years passed, and when Rosa turned seven, she still loved school very much. She became a good reader and was not afraid to read right out loud when it was her turn.

The winter of 1902 was terribly cold. There never was enough coal or wood for heat. Mama was not feeling good at all and could not work very long each day. Rosa and her two sisters stayed home from school most of the time to help out, and they worked as hard as they could to help Mama do washin's. Brother Bert had gone to work and to live at a local lumber company the year before. Now Rosa was in charge of gathering all the wood, as Belle and Louisa were not very good at chopping and sawing. But they were always up to their elbows in suds or hanging clothes or cookin' or mendin', and Rosa was glad she did not have to do much of that.

Almost every week that winter, Rosa made sister Louisa trudge with her way down the railroad track. They must wait for the daily train to go by. When it came chugging up the long grade toward town, it moved very slowly. Rosa and Louisa would run along a road just below the tracks. They were waiting for the tall, skinny workman who rode in the back part of the engine, the coal car. He always waved at them, and then he would toss out two big scoop-shovels full of coal right down the bank. The girls would wave and smile and clap their hands, and the workman would wave and smile broadly at them as the train puffed itself on into town. Then Rosa and Louisa would scurry to pick up all the coal and put each and every chunk into their gunny sacks. The coal-filled sacks were very heavy to drag back to their house, but they couldn't wait for Mama to see what they had. And then Mama always scolded them. "You girls know that isn't our coal; it belongs to the railroad. We can't take their coal." And they would always tell her exactly how the workman just threw it off as a "gift" and always motioned that it was alright for them to pick it up. "He smiles and waves at us, Mama; he wants us to have the coal."

The fall when Rosa turned eight, Belle and Louisa both went out to live-in maid service. They would earn their board and keep only for the first few years, but they were happy to be able to get that. They knew how hard it was for their mama to care for three children. Now there were just Rosa and Mama. They were "making-do," as Mama always said. Often there were letters from Rosa's older brothers and sisters with a little money for Mama. That helped a lot because Mama had many "sick-spells" and could not work very long at a time. Rosa stayed home from school most of that winter to help out. She would tell her mama, "Now, Mama, you just lay there; you just rest a little. I can do up this batch of washin' lickety-split, you'll see. Now you just rest a spell."

Rosa's mama, Mary Catherine, was a small, slender woman who had worked very, very hard all her life. She was the only girl in her family, having two older brothers. She and her brothers had been raised on a farm in Indiana by loving immigrant parents, Mother from Ireland and Father from Germany. It was just a way of life for farmers to work from dawn till dusk. Mary married James Henry Scott and had ten children in fifteen years, and all of those years had been very hard for Mary. The Scott family had been labeled Rebels by the townspeople, and they had all experienced that cruel hatred all their lives. But Mary loved her children dearly and helped them to endure this bias, raising them all to be caring, helpful, and kind people.

Mary had brown eyes and lots of soft, brown hair, always worn in a tight bun at the back of her neck. Rosa was very much like her mother, but she had cornflower-blue eyes, and that was the first thing a person would notice about her. She also had light brown hair that was thick and silky, and always, of course, worn in a long braid down her back. She was a very tiny girl, looking frail with her skinny arms and legs, but she was wiry tough and could swing an axe with vigor, and she seemed to have boundless energy.

Rosa had two things that she dearly loved to do. Oh, how she loved to climb up as high as she could in the old apple tree in the backyard! And now every time she did, she would think about how her sisters used to call her from the back porch when it was her time to help with the kitchen chores. "Rosa, Rosa Ellen, where are you? You're supposed to help us with the cannin' today; there is so much peelin' and grindin' to do. Rosa! Come in and help. Rosa, are you playin' hide-away up in that apple tree again? I know you are; you're always up there. Don't you know that girls are not supposed to climb trees? Oh, Rosa Ellen, you act just like a boy; shame on you!" But Rosa would smile to herself and get comfy on a big gnarled limb and watch the sunlight dapple through the green leaves. She could always spend any extra time up here watchin' the clouds drift by.

Her other best thing she liked to do was on a Sunday. After church was over, she would run the short way through town to the train station to watch the train go by. She loved to sit on a box and get the shivers each time the big engine slowed down to pick up the mail pouch that would be hanging on a big metal arm. The trainman would just grab it as the train went by. The engine always emitted great puffs of smoke and hissed something fierce. And then there were the people in the coach windows to watch. Some of the ladies had big, fluffy hats and fur collars on their coats. They looked so pretty and warm and cozy inside the train. Once in a while a lady would raise a gloved hand and wave. Rosa would smile broadly and wave right back. Oh, that always made it a very special day for Rosa.

On one rainy Sunday when Rosa was sitting up on her favorite perch at the depot, the train actually came to a jerking, hissing stop. A porter jumped out and placed his step. Then a big, tall man in a black hat and black coat, with a cape-like thing over the shoulders, stepped hurriedly off that train. He was carrying two very large carpet bags. Rosa was really surprised because very few people ever got off the train in this little town of Magley. The tall man spoke briefly to the station master and then started walking with long, swift strides into town, carrying his two bags. Rosa was very, very curious about this strange visitor.

She jumped down from her perch and followed him. She had to run just to keep him in sight. He did not look around, just hurried along. He walked right through the small town and just kept going right up the road. Rosa followed and thought, "Well, anyway, this is on my way home." The man neared the fence to her very own house, and he swung open the gate and strode right up to Rosa's own door. She saw him put the bags down and then reach up and knock very hard on her door.

Rosa was in a panic. Who was this man at their door? Was he going to harm her mama? Then she saw Mama open the door and step back with a gasp, her hands fluttering in front of her. Mama saw Rosa running up the path behind the man, and she motioned to Rosa that it was alright, that Rosa was supposed to wait outside. Rosa guessed her mama was not afraid of the tall man. It seemed it was a long time she waited; she could still hear the train huffing and puffing at the depot. Then it whistled, long and loud. Maybe the train was waiting for the man, the stranger, who came to their house and wanted to talk with her mama. Rosa's heart was pounding right out of her chest. Oh my, she was so afraid.

The man strode out the door without the bags; he looked at Rosa standing on the porch. He reached out a black gloved hand and lifted her little chin up to look at her face. He was old, she saw, and he had very blue eyes. Then quickly he was gone, almost trotting down the road. Rosa just stood there and watched him go for a moment and then was very scared for her mama. She ran into the house as fast as she could.

Mama was sitting in her rocker, quietly crying into her apron. "Mama, Mama, what did that man do to you?" Rosa rushed to her and laid her head on Mama's lap and wanted her to stop crying. "Please, Mama, it's alright; who was that man? Please, Mama, don't cry."

Her mama slowly told her that the man was Rosa's very own uncle from way down south. He was one of Papa Scott's brothers. "Oh, Rosa, it has taken him all these years to find out whatever happened to his youngest brother. He brought us some money and some food and things and will send more when he can. He and his brothers and your grandfather lost everything in the war—other sons, other nephews, and all their lands. He is very old, Rosa, but he looked so much like your papa. These are tears of joy, for having seen him, just once, and to know he cared enough to look for us all these many years."

The rest of that winter, and from then on, Rosa and Mama did have enough coal for heat, and they were able to get some medicine that seemed to help Mama's sick-spells. It was a much easier time for the two of them, but Mama cried a lot. Rosa oftentimes could hear her at night. Then Rosa would sob into her own pillow and pray that her mama would not be so sad.

The next few years were trying years for Rosa. She did very well in school, but the other children seemed to be more cruel to her with each passing day. "Skinny Scotty, the Rebel Brat" seemed to be more her name than "Rosa Ellen Scott." On top of that, somehow she was tagged a tomboy, too. "Look at Skinny Scotty; she looks like a boy and acts like a boy; maybe she really is a 'Rebel boy in a girl's dress,'" they would chant at her. Needless to say, she began to fight like a boy. When she could not take the tauntings anymore, she would just start punching anyone she could catch. She could run like the dickens, so she got into lots of fisticuffs. It was not a good time for Rosa at all. But she did love her schoolwork and did not mind walking to and from school all by herself. She would take that time to recite her lessons over and over. Then as soon as she got home, she would help her Mama do washin's till time for prayers and bed.

Each fall her mama would hire out to different farms at butchering time. She took Rosa, and they would stay several days at each farm. So for long periods of time, Rosa was needed to help her mama and did not go to school. This did not bother Rosa one bit; at least she was away from the "Skinny Scotty" name-calling. Mama was well known for her skill at butchering and making head cheese and blood sausages and curing bacons and hams and such. Mama's papa was German, and he had passed on this special knowledge to her.

It was grueling work, mostly in outside kitchens. Rosa's chore was usually in the stirring and the stuffing of the sausages. She also scraped hides and ran and fetched for everyone all day. Mama hated to go to some of the farms because the women of those households were most unkind to her and Rosa. Those women never lost their hatred of Rebels, and somehow they classified Mother Scott and all her children as "those hated Rebels."

There was one farm they always worked at, the Wolf Farm. Mr. Wolf was a kindly man, and he rode a large brown stallion. Rosa thought Mr. Wolf was about the most wonderful person in the whole wide world. He always smiled at Rosa and talked with her for a minute. A few times he even lifted Rosa up on his shiny brown saddle and walked the big horse around the paddock. Oh, that was heaven for Rosa.

Mr. Wolf's wife was not well, and so the Wolfs had lots of household help, but Mama was called to work there regularly. Mama and Mrs. Wolf became very good friends. Often, after the chores were finished, Mama and Mrs. Wolf would sit out on the front porch and talk, and Rosa would sit on the top step and listen to the lady-talk. Sometimes one of the kitchen maids would serve them something special. Rosa's favorite was fresh strawberries with dollops of heavy cream on top. Rosa would savor every single berry with pleasure. Then one day, the nice Mrs. Wolf passed away. Mama and Rosa went to her funeral service, and Mama was very sad for a long time.

Sometime after that, Mr. Wolf came riding by their house and stopped to say hello to Rosa. She was so happy to see him, she came right out and asked if she could make him some tea. They were sitting on the porch when Mama came home, so they all sat and had tea and visited. They heard all about a long trip he had taken to Boston and all the way to New York City. It was so exciting that Rosa could not sit still. Her Mama smiled and asked Rosa to please go bring more hot water for tea.

After that, Mr. Wolf often stopped by and visited with them. He would stretch out his long legs in Mama's warm kitchen and just talk and talk. Rosa dearly loved to see the big, brown horse tied up at their hitching post. Her heart would sing and be so happy when he was there.

One time, Mr. Wolf went on a long train ride to San Francisco in California. He said he wanted to see that other ocean. Well, when he came home this time, he brought a new bride. Rosa heard about "the bride" at school and saw the buggy with "her" in it one day. She was holding a big yellow parasol over a very fancy hat. Mr. Wolf just tipped his hat to Rosa as the buggy passed her on the road.

After that, Rosa cried her heart out. Her Mama tried to explain that Mr. Wolf was a lonely widower, he needed a wife, now he would be much happier. Rosa finally blurted out, "Oh, Mama, I love Mr. Wolf, and I wanted him to be my papa."

"Oh, Rosey, now, now little Rosey," Mama told her quietly, "I'm so sorry, don't cry, but don't you see, Mr. Wolf is a wealthy man, a very educated landowner, and he would never even think of marrying anyone like your mama. I am only a washer-woman, the kitchen help, the sausage-maker. Now hush, don't cry any more. Don't you see, that could never, never, ever be." But Rosa's heart was truly broken, not only for herself, but for the heartache she had heard in her mama's voice that day.

Their life was a hard struggle, but somehow they managed, "making-do" as Mama always said. And then there was an outbreak of influenza in the town, and one day Rosa came home from school feeling very sick. Even though Mama had nursed others through this terrible illness, she knew it was life threatening. She immediately began doing all the things she could for Rosa. There came a time during the fevers and sweats that Mama thought she might lose her. She prayed while she worked over Rosa, "Please, dear Lord, not this young one; please help her, Lord; send her guardian angel to her. Oh please, Lord, this one is special. This is a special child, and we desperately need your help."

When Rosa was finally free of the terrible fevers, she told her mama, "Oh, Mama, there was one time when I felt so free and light, I reached up and took the hand of a pretty lady. She looked like you, Mama, with brown eyes and soft hair. We walked a little, and she knelt down and put her soft arms around me. Oh, I loved her so much, and she whispered those shushing sing-songs in my ear, just like sister Belle always did. Oh, Mama, I felt so good with her. There was no ache, none at all, and then she was gone, and I felt the hurt so bad again."

Her mama held her and said, "Oh, Rosey, my little Rose-bud, that was your guardian angel. She came down to help us. Our dear Lord sent her to make you better, that's what happened. Oh, I prayed she would come, and the Lord did send her. You know, Rosey, your guardian angel is always your grandmother or sometimes your great-grandmother, and this time she came to make you well, and she will come and help you whenever you need her. So don't ever forget her, Rosey, because she will always be looking over you, and you must remember her in your prayers."

CHAPTER TWO

West to Idaho

ROSA SLOWLY GAINED BACK HER STRENGTH over the next few months, and late that same year of 1904 some exciting news was about to make Rosa and her mama very, very happy.

One day a long letter came from brother Henry. Henry was Rosa's next to oldest brother; he was working as a telegraph operator for the Union Pacific Railroad way out west in Washington state. His letter read,

My Dear Mama and Rosa,

I saw a poster in a railroad depot about homestead land that the railroad was givin away free over in Ideho state. I have already been over there lookin around and they gave me 160 acres of land across the Snake river from Blackfoot, Ideho. Now I will be comin back East in two month's time to help you both to pack up and move out west to help me prove-up on our own land, our own homestead in Ideho.

All Mama could say after they had read the letter over and over to each other was, "A miracle has come to us, Rosa; now we can leave Magley, Indiana, forever and ever."

So in the early spring of 1905 when Rosa was still nine years old, they were busy planning their trip to Idaho. The roads around Magley were still muddy and icy in places. But this spring they would not be planting the garden out back, and they would not have to fight the slugs and the mealy worms for the vegetables, either. Rosa and Mama talked every day about what they would grow on the homestead in I-de-ho. They always laughed when Mama called it I-de-ho, like Henry had written, and Mama said, probably a hundred times, "You know, Rosey, Henry says they grow the best turnips and potatoes of the whole land in I-de-ho, and big fat onions that are sweet as apples. We surely will be growin' those. We'll take all the garden seeds we can find, and the flower seeds, and see what we can grow out there on our new land in the west."

They planned and planned, and Mama seemed so happy. Henry sent a detailed letter on what they should pack and what they should try to trade or sell, so that decision was made for them. Rosa still made her weekly trips down to watch the trains, but now she was always picturing herself and her mama sitting in one of the lighted coaches looking so ladylike. The station master knew Rosa and talked with her about the train ride she would soon be taking all the way out west. He told her, "Now, you watch for real buffalo alongside the tracks and out on the plains. I doubt it, but there still might be some to be seen if you keep a sharp eye out. But there will be lots of those antelope to see." And then he would laugh and pat the skinny little girl on the head. "But you better look out for those redskins, Rosa. They will surely steal a blue-eyed gal like you in a jiffy."

Sister Louisa made a swift decision when she was written about these plans. She was working for a farmer in a nearby town. If Henry could take her along, she wanted to go too. Somehow Henry arranged this, and Mama and Rosa were so very happy that Louisa could go with them.

Mama had been very busy packing, of course, but each evening she would sit and stitch away. They must have some "proper traveling things," she told Rosa. A neighbor lady, who was kind of friendly with Mama, was very helpful; she gave Mama several wool coats her children had outgrown, and some dresses and things. Mama was an expert seamstress, a skill she had learned from her mother, so it did not take her any time at all to alter the coats and to re-do those dresses to fit herself and Rosa. She had to completely tear apart one coat and sew the whole thing up again to fit Rosa's thin little frame. But it turned out to be a fine, brown, wool coat with a nice wide collar, and it was long enough to go down to her ankles. Oh, she felt very ladylike in the coat. There was a small, brown hat too, and with her woolen scarf, she felt she truly looked like the fancy ladies she had seen in all the train cars for so many years. Mama stitched up her own nice traveling coat and even had time to alter one for Louisa. Oh, they would indeed be very elegant ladies for their grand train trip out west.

Henry had been home a few days and had crated up as many of Mama's things as he was able to ship on the train. Because he worked for the railroads, he was allowed passes for his family and possessions. Finally the big day arrived. They were leaving Magley, Indiana, this fifth day of April, 1905.

Rosa felt butterflies flitting around in her middle when they stepped aboard the train. The locomotive was huffing and puffing and shooshing off great clouds of steam. She could see that the train was not very long, and it had that pretty, little, red caboose at the end. She wished she could run up to the coal car to see if that kind workman, who threw off the coal for them for so many years, was there. Oh, she wished she could thank him. But there was no time for that, as Henry hurriedly got them inside the coach and seated. Then she could hear the engine puffing very hard, there was a screeching noise from the wheels as they tried to go, and the whole train shuddered. Rosa could feel the mighty wheels slowly turn and the train pick up more motion. She was suddenly fearful; it was so jerky; it lurched from side to side and made awful noises. The clacking sounds were loud and scary. It was a long time before she could let go her tight grip on the armrest. After a while, she looked around out the window, and there was the whole land going by out there. Oh my, there was so much to look at! Soon she started to like the continual motion and quick, side-to-side jerks of the train. Rosa had never been out of Magley, and she tried to take in all that she was seeing. The land was so vast, and she didn't want to miss one single thing.

It was late in the day when the train pulled into the Chicago outskirts. Rosa could not believe her eyes. As far as she could see, there were houses and smokestacks. The roads were covered with wagons and buggies and people on horseback and people walking everywhere. "Oh my, oh my," she thought, "I wouldn't want to be lost out there."

Rosa knew by heart all the different stops they would make, for Henry had told her exactly where the train would travel. She was also glad she had listened to the schoolmarm and learned about the different states they would be traveling through all the way out to Idaho.

Brother Henry was worried about the Chicago stop. They must change trains here, and they would not have much time. Also, he had another problem; he was bringing along his prized possession, his bicycle. Mama had kept the bicycle for him in the back shed for a long time. He had told her that he would need the bicycle to get back and forth between the town of Springfield and their homestead.

Henry gave the ladies careful instructions on exactly what to do in the Chicago train station. "Now, you each carry your own bundle and don't lay it down for a second. You are all to walk with me, and each of you should hang onto the bicycle with one hand and never let go, else you will be lost in the crowd, and we must get over to the westbound train as fast as we can." As soon as they stepped off the train, they were suddenly in a mad crush of people. Folks were rushing to and fro, pushing and crowding around. Rosa wanted to shut her eyes and not look at them, but she knew she had to hang onto the bicycle seat as tight as she could with the one hand and carry her bundle with her quilt wrapped around it with the other hand. It was getting dark, and she thought the people rushing by were not very nice at all. She hoped folks "way out west" would be more courteous.

After hurrying aboard the westbound train, Henry got them seated, but he was immediately jumped by a big, burly porter in a sweaty uniform. "You can't bring that bicycle in here; that has to go in baggage." Rosa knew Henry had his story all ready for this problem. "You see, sir, I also work for this railroad. See, here are my passes. I'm taking my mother and sisters out west to homestead in Idaho. I've shipped all I was allowed of Mother's household things that she will need out on the homestead. Now, I can set my bicycle here in the vestibule, and it will not be in anybody's way at all, and the porter on the train up from Indiana was agreeable to let me set it there." The porter looked them over and raved on awhile about the regulations but finally relented. "Well, I suppose that will be all right."

By then it was dark, and they were all so very tired. Poor Mama looked pale. The girls made her eat something from their food basket.

After she sipped a hot cup of tea, they got her as comfortable as one can get in the upright coach chair. Finally, with her feet up on her bundle and her quilt tucked around her, she went to sleep.

But oh, Rosa could not sleep; she was too excited and too happy to ever sleep. She looked around the coach car. A coal stove was at the front, and she watched the porter stoke it with more coal. They had heated Mama's tea on it, and she was glad for that. The only light in the coach came from a kerosene lantern hanging from the ceiling. Rosa could see that most everyone was trying to sleep all curled up in their seats with quilts or coats draped over them. Outside some blurry lights went by; sometimes a bright lighted window would flash out in the dark. Oh my yes, it was raining some; she could see it now, spattering the window. Of course it was easy for Rosa to curl up in her seat. She had plenty of room to pull up her knees and tuck her quilt around them and up under her neck. She finally closed her eyes, listening to the clickety-clack, clickety-clack and now enjoying the short, side-to-side jerks of the train. She kept singing to herself along with the clickety clacks.

Go-in' out west, go-in' to I-de-ho,
go-in' to I-de-ho, to homestead there—
in I-de-ho, go-in' to I-de-ho.

Just at dawn Rosa woke and pressed her face to the window. Why, what was this? she wondered. There was nothing but water as far as she could see. My goodness, where were they? Maybe they were on the wrong train. She reached over the back of her seat and shook Henry's shoulder. "Look, Henry, we are out on an ocean; we must be lost. Are we lost, Henry?"

Henry rubbed his tired eyes and looked out his window. "Oh no, no, Rosa, we are not lost at all; this must be the ol' Mississippi River. Remember, I told you we would cross it. Yes, it is wide; it's miles wide. Look way up there. See, that looks like a barge. They ship all kinds of goods downriver in those big, flat barges."

Mama had packed as much food for the trip as she and Henry could carry, but Henry said he would swing off at any stop he could and pick up a few more things. He did come back with some interesting things but mostly bread, cheese and the sage tea for Mama, which she said was kind

21

of bitter but good anyway. One time Henry bought some hoe-cakes made from Indian corn, and Rosa liked those and wondered if Indians had really made them. A few times Henry came back with fresh, warm milk, and Rosa thought it was very sweet indeed. They all relished this treat.

Sometimes during the day, a porter in a blue uniform would come through the car. There was one who was very black-skinned. Rosa wanted to speak to him because she had never seen a man who had black skin. One morning she got up her courage and said good morning to him. He smiled down at her and flashed a grin. He had large teeth, very shiny and white. "Mornin', little Miss," he said. "Are you-all havin' a nice train ride?" Rosa was suddenly very shy but did say, "Yes sir, yes sir, I truly am." Oh, Rosa wanted to ask him so many things, but she just couldn't. She knew he was a negra man and that the Civil War had been fought over these negra people who were kept as slaves in the South. Her own Papa Scott had fought in that war, and it had been a terrible, terrible war, and when it was over, these people were not slaves to anyone anymore. Oh, there was so much she wanted to ask him, but she just couldn't get up the courage.

Each morning, noon and evening, that same porter would stoke up the coal stove in the car. It was nice to feel the warmth filling the car, and if you had a tin pot like her Mama carried, you could just brew up some tea in a jiffy.

The plains of Iowa were surprising to Rosa. She had read they were rolling like the oceans of water, and yes, they were rolling hills but covered with the bright green new growth of wheat and other grains. Oh, it was a splendid sight, with cozy farm houses and big barns. Sometimes there would be a road with wagons hurrying along pulled by nice, fat horses, and sometimes she saw a few tall trees. She kept her eyes glued to the cindery window; she did not want to miss a minute of the wonders gliding by out there in these vast lands.

Rosa saw her first Indian at the station in Council Bluff, Iowa. There were three of them standing beside the station house. One had a wide-brimmed hat, and all three had blankets wrapped around their shoulders. The blankets were very colorful—reds, greens, and yellows—but did look well worn. Rosa tried to decide which one was a lady Indian but could not tell because they all had long hair. The Indians watched the train but didn't move the whole time the train was stopped at the station.

Henry told her they would see many Indians, different tribes of Indians, but they would not harm anyone because they had been "tamed."

Rosa studied the other passengers in the car as often as she could without being impolite. No one spoke to her, although her mama and Louisa did talk with one woman seated across the aisle. The lady was a farmer's wife, Rosa could tell. She had seen many women like that, always tired and sad looking. Further up in the car, a lady in a fancy hat with blue feathers on top was sitting with a young lady. There were pretty red ribbons in the girl's dark hair. Rosa wanted to go up and speak with them but was afraid it would not be polite. There were many big, gruff-looking men in the car, some talking very loud to each other. Rosa decided these men were not farmers, maybe miners, going out West to see if there was any of that gold left to be found out in California.

Rosa was now very comfortable with the continual motion and noise of the train. She could easily walk up and down the aisle without falling against the seats. The water-closet, called the lavatory, in the next car was a source of delight to Rosa. There was running water; you just had to pump a little metal handle thing. But she was confused about the chamber potty, because when you pushed the button where it said to push, a trap door opened and everything went right out onto the tracks. She could see the black wooden ties whizzing by under the train. She had lived near the railroad tracks all her life and did not know of this; this was very strange indeed. But her delight was standing up on her toes so she could see herself in the fine, big mirror. Oh, all this was wondrous, and so much nicer than any privy she had "ever, ever" seen. The word "lavatory" was new to Rosa, and she practiced spelling it to herself—a fine word, indeed.

Watching the men in the coach she thought were miners, she remembered the many stories she had heard about the gold rush in California. When she remembered these stories, she always pictured her Uncle John. He was one of Mama's older brothers who had gone out West many years before to make his fortune in the gold fields. In her imagination she could see her Uncle John, very rich, with gold nuggets in his pockets, living in a fancy house and owning a fine carriage pulled by a pair of high-stepping, matched bays.

Mama's brothers, John and Albert, had been very young men when they left the family farm in Indiana and started walking west. They followed the immigrant wagon trains on the long trek to find their fortunes in gold. When these uncles had reached a wagon stop near Cusad, Nebraska, Albert said, "John, this is as far as I'm goin'; I'm gonna homestead around here. This is real fertile farmland; I'm not goin' no further." But John was a dreamer and wanted to see the gold layin' on the ground and waitin' in the streambeds of Californy. "You can just pick it up, Albert; we'll be wealthy men, and you can buy all the land you want in Californy."

They argued back and forth for two days, and finally John went on alone. No one in the family ever heard of John again, nor ever learned what had happened to him. But Mama always told them, "He must have died, because John could write, and he would have written us a letter sometime, from somewhere, if he had lived to reach Californy." Rosa was always sad about Uncle John, but she loved to hear the story of Uncle Albert. Her mama had told it so many times that Rosa knew it all by heart.

Albert had to find work as he looked over the Nebraska countryside for his homestead. He had no trouble hiring out to many immigrants, because he was big and husky and very knowledgeable about repairing wagon wheels and such. One day a large wagon train pulled into Cusad to rest up and to repair their wagons for the next long haul. In that train a young girl was looking for a driver for her wagon. Her father had recently died of a fever on the trail, and she needed help. It took Albert only three days to propose to Emily. Now he had a new bride, and he also became the proud owner of a wagon load of farm and household things, a cow, and a team of very strong horses—two big grays from excellent stock. Emily was completely happy to settle down with Albert in Nebraska and not go any further with the wagon train.

Mama and Uncle Albert had written letters back and forth over all the years since Albert and his brother had left home to find their fortune in the gold fields of Californy. Albert had written her all about settling down with Emily and all about the horse farm and their many children. They had a whole passel of grandchildren, too.

Rosa was very excited because they would soon be visiting Uncle Albert. The train made a stop near Cusad, Nebraska, and they were all going to get off the train and stay a few days with Uncle Albert's family. So, after those many long years, Mama was going to get to visit with her brother.

The very next stop now would be for Cusad. Everyone was very anxious. They hoped Uncle Albert would be there to meet them. Henry had telegraphed when they would arrive. Oh, they were all so anxious to see if he would be there. Mama was smiling and almost giggly in her excitement. Rosa and Louisa got the biggest laugh at her antics.

"Oh, there he is," Mama shouted as the train came to its jerking stop. "There's brother Albert; he's the big one with the curly hair. There's Albert; I would know him anywhere; he is so like our papa." Mama jumped down from the train like a young girl and ran into the arms of a big, husky bear of a man. Mama was so little, and Uncle was such a huge man, he just picked her up and swung her around in a circle like a little doll. Mama was laughing and crying all at the same time.

Albert and Emily had four big sons and three short, plump daughters and that passel of grandchildren. It was a very lively, healthy family who laughed a lot. Two of the sons came along to the train depot with Uncle to meet the family and drive everyone back to the homestead. They brought a big farm wagon with lots of room for everyone. It was pulled by a team of husky dapple gray horses. Rosa was very, very impressed with the huge horses and asked to ride up front with her cousin John who was driving the team. It took a couple of hours to drive out through the prairie land to Uncle's homestead, but Rosa was completely happy to ride the bumpy seat, look out across the green fields, and listen to the happy chatter of Mama and Uncle Albert.

The time spent on Uncle Albert's farm was such an exciting time for Rosa. There was so much food and so many children. Everyone made a fuss over little Rosa, always coaxing her to eat a little more. "Have some more of the peach pie, Rosa; we have to put some bulk on you. You will need it to go homesteadin' out in the wild west." And then they would all laugh merrily with her. She had never had this kind of attention; it was very enjoyable, and everyone was being so loving to her and Mama and Louisa and Henry.

Uncle had a whole barn full of horses. He raised big work horses, and they were all over the farm, in paddocks and in the fields. There were chunky colts with long, feathery hair on their fetlocks. Rosa even got to ride on the broad back of one of the huge, friendly mares. It was like sitting on a table top—Rosa's legs just stuck straight out. Oh, Rosa never ever wanted to leave such a heavenly place. She spent all the time she could around the horses, and her cousins teased her about that, but it was fun teasing.

One day Uncle Albert came by and talked with her about his horses. "I been breedin' and raisin' up this work stock ever since I been here, Rosa. Emily and I started this herd with the two wagon horses she and her pa brought from back East so many years ago. These horses are some of the finest stock you'll ever see anywhere. They make me and all my boys a fine living. And I see that you have a good eye for solid horseflesh, Rosa. What do you think of that black over there, the one with the white sox? Pretty nice colt ain't he?"

Somehow Rosa did not feel shy around Uncle Albert, and she told him about ol' Abraham pulling the wagon with her papa in it. She told him how she would surely love to have a fine black horse of her very own someday. Albert was quiet for a while, then told her, "Rosa Ellen, I wish I could send that there black colt with you, but that would be might nigh impossible, and then, of course, he is not a saddle horse like you will need out in I-de-ho. But I tell you what, little gal, after you all get settled out there on your homestead, I'm gonna make sure that you get a saddle horse of your very own. I'll make some plans with Henry, and you will have your horse. 'Course you'll have to take care of it all by yourself. Now, can you do that?"

Rosa looked up at the big, bearded man and tears rolled down her cheeks. "Yes sir, yes sir, I can look after a horse. I can look after one real good." She was so choked up she couldn't say more, but Uncle Albert patted her head and said, "Then, that there is a promise I make to you, little Rosey girl."

Uncle Albert and his family tried to get Mama and Henry to change their minds and stay in Nebraska. But Henry had his job with the railroad way out west and said he could not support Mama and the girls without his job. Also, he wanted to homestead somewhere, and there was no more land to homestead in Nebraska anymore. He was very proud, Rosa knew, and had to have his own land, his own homestead.

Then all too soon they were taken the long way back to catch the train. After many sad farewells, with Mama crying the whole time, they were again aboard the lurching train heading west.

As the train passed through the western part of Nebraska, Rosa was thrilled to see so many wildflowers. The continuous rolling hills were covered with small blooms of all colors. Mama and Louisa could not believe what they were seeing. The Platte River wound round and round through the small hills, and the river banks were lined with bright green, willowy-looking trees. Oh, it was a beautiful sight.

It was almost dark one evening when the train made a stop in Medicine Bow, Wyoming. Henry said they could all get off and walk up and down the loading platform and stretch a little. It was funny to feel the solid ground under them again. Rosa told them, "This must be what sailors call losin' their sea-legs."

There were Indians, lots of them, sitting around cross-legged, standing together, walking slowly by. Rosa looked for a papoose and did see one carried flat on a board tied to the back of a squaw. Oh, how she wanted to run over and ask if she could look at the Indian baby, but her mama said, "No, no, Rosa, that would not be polite to do that."

She looked closely at these Indians. They were very different from the others she had seen, taller maybe, with all kinds of feathers and funny stovepipe-looking hats. Their blankets looked clean and bright and colorful. She even heard a couple of men talking; it was a strange guttural sound, and then they both laughed. "My," she said to herself, "they have very large, strong teeth, and they even look friendly."

Back on the train again, they talked about the Indians. They also talked about the real cowhands they had seen, with their horses tied to the hitch-rail near the depot. They had awkward looking saddles, and the horses seemed very scrawny to Rosa. One horse was a paint with large black splotches on his rump, and he had a long, black tail. She had seen only pictures of the spotted horses and hoped someday to get a closer look at one.

On the high plains of Wyoming, Rosa finally saw her first antelope. "Prong-horns" they were called. At first she tried to keep count of how many she saw but soon gave that up. Some were just grazing, and some looked up at the rattling train. Others were bounding along stiff-legged, and then all of a sudden they would make a big leap. It was as if they thought it was great fun to run alongside the train.

A porter pointed out to her, way off in the far distance, some deep-brownish looking animals. "I think that there is a herd of buffalo, Miss. I told you we might spot some; then again, them might be a herd of cattle. Too fer away to really tell, and besides, 'most all of the buffalos have been kilt off by now." He also told her about the funny, little, rabbity animals called prairie dogs. "And fer sure, those little fellers are mighty fine eatin'; make the tastiest stew you ever et, but you have to trap 'em 'cause you sure can't shoot 'em; they are mighty quick critters."

Rosa never tired of spotting the little prairie dogs. They were so comical; they would just jump right up in the air and gleefully turn upside down and dive right straight into a hole. Their furry tail flipped as they disappeared, and Rosa laughed every time she saw them do that.

As the train slowly puffed its way up into the Rocky Mountains, Rosa was astounded. She had never seen mountains and could not believe that the train would not fall down into the steep canyons. Sometimes the peaks went right straight up and were so high that she could not even see the tops. The train had to go very, very slow and very carefully, and it creaked and bumped around each tight curve. On some switchbacks, Rosa could see the engine chugging its way ahead around another sharp bend. A river tumbled way, way down below. It looked swollen and powerful; it must have pushed those huge boulders into those torturous jumbles. Oh, she was frightened that the train would fall into one of those chasms, and yet she was so excited about actually going through the big Rocky Mountains of the West. It was all too much for a little girl to take in, and she looked and looked and tried not to miss even one mountainside or one gorge with water cascading down and down into the river below, or anything at all.

At night Rosa would curl up in her seat, her quilt tucked all around her, and be asleep as soon as she closed her eyes.

Then one day Henry said they would soon be changing trains. The next stop would be Salt Lake City, Utah. Rosa had read about the Mormons, of the Church of Jesus Christ of Latter Day Saints, and how God himself had finally led Brigham Young and his people to this promised land. She truly expected to see lush green gardens and trees heavy with spring blossoms, a paradise, a garden of Eden. But she looked and looked and saw nothing but a few small, snug farms with some green fields, neat looking but certainly not a garden of Eden. Then she saw a little part of the white alkaline lake; it looked all white and parched and scary.

They walked with Henry leading, pushing his bicycle, through the huge depot at Salt Lake City, and oh, that depot was truly an amazing building. There were big, colorful paintings, "murals" her mama called them, high up, all around the walls. It was a huge place, and the folks walking by were friendly and smiling. But there was not time to see enough of this pretty place as they must hurry, keep hold of their bundles, and get through the huge building and out onto another platform to catch another train.

Rosa could hardly sleep that night on the train, not because of the motion and the clatter—she was used to that—but because Henry had told them that they would be leaving the train for good the very next day. They would be getting off at the Blackfoot, Idaho stop. He had cautioned them several times. "Now hang tight to your bundle when we get off in Blackfoot. There will be a passel of Indians around; these will be the Shoshone and the Bannock tribes. There is a big Indian reservation near Blackfoot. They will not harm you, but they might make off with your bundle if you set it down for even a second."

They stepped down from the train about mid-afternoon, and suddenly Rosa was really afraid. There were Indians, lots of them, crowding around. Some were dirty and, oh my, that terrible smell, like rancid sweat, and it was very strong. But a few of them were clean looking with bright colored blankets and nice, shiny black hair. She wondered why they were so different. She would remember to ask Henry about that. All the Indians were trying to get aboard the train quickly, as it did not stop long in Blackfoot.

Henry led them away from the depot, and they were happy to hurry along behind him. He finally led them down a long boardwalk past a few business shops to a small, wooden-framed building he proudly said was a "hotel."

A real hotel. Rosa had heard about a hotel but had never seen one. She knew it was a place where rich folks stayed in rooms at night, and just like the rich folks, they did have their own room. 'Course they had to go downstairs and out back across the yard for the "lavatory." Rosa loved to use that word, and Mama smiled each time she said it. They even sat in a real hotel dining room with other folks. They sat at a round table and had a chicken-and-dumpling stew for their supper. Rosa savored every mouthful of the thick, hearty stew. Since leaving Uncle Albert's farm, they had not had a hot meal.

Henry said they must get to sleep as early as they could because they would leave Blackfoot for the town of Springfield at dawn the next morning. It was hard for Rosa to sleep, although the pallet she had on the floor was very soft compared to the hard upright coach chair she had curled up in on the train.

She was very excited about tomorrow, as they would ride in a real stagecoach. Henry said the stagecoach would be driven right onto a flat-boat ferry, horses and all, to cross over the Snake River. Of course she was curious about the name of the river. She wondered if it was filled up with snakes, and that made her shiver. A small garden snake made a fine pet, but a river full of snakes would be very frightful.

Sure enough, just at the break of light, they were all scrunched together in a big, wooden stagecoach. Henry rode up top with two other men. He had tied his trusty bicycle on top of all the bundles and cases, clear up top of the coach. Rosa wanted to ride up there too, but Mama said that would not be ladylike at all. "Oh, Rosa Ellen," she said and smiled, "you just cannot do the things boys do. That won't do at all."

Rosa was not impressed at all with the six horses hitched to the stagecoach. They looked thin and scrawny, just like those cowhands' horses she had seen in Wyoming. The coach swayed and lurched from side to side, and they were glad they were all packed in so tight. Soon it was going very fast, and Rosa thought maybe the skinny horses were much stronger than they looked. Rosa was glad Mama had given her the window seat, although the dust billowed up something fierce and made it hard to see anything. But she did see some nice looking farms along the riverside, and then just some strange rolling hills with grayish bushes growing all over. There were also funny looking slabs of stones, jumbled up in ragged piles all around.

Mama told her, "No, there are no snakes in the Snake River; oh, maybe a few of those rattlesnakes Henry told us about, but I don't think they like water like those water moccasins do that live down in the South. The river is called Snake because it slithers through many curves and twists and has cut its wiggly way down into deep gorges, but here in this part of the country, it flattens out and behaves just like any other river."

Soon they were on the wide flat-boat. The driver had just carefully walked his horses right out onto the flat-boat, and then they were slowly moving across the wide river. Rosa wanted to get out and look down at the churning water, but Mama said, "We must stay inside the coach. Henry said it would only take a short time to cross over." Rosa looked down into the swirling muddy water and shivered. There could be snakes in there: it looked awful scary.

They made one stop at a way station and had a bowl of beans with big chunks of fat bacon and some kind of flat, hard bread. Then, after taking their turns going out back, they were again crammed into the coach.

They arrived in the little town of Springfield late in the afternoon. All of them were very dusty and very tired and aching all over. Riding in a stagecoach is not what I thought it would be like, Rosa mused to herself; the thing lurches and bounces everyone around, just like a sack of potatoes being drug by a mule.

Henry walked them down past a few small buildings. There was a mercantile shop made out of those large, gray slabs or rocks, and it sure looked big and solid. They went past a blacksmith shop and around a corner to a white, wooden house. It had wide steps and a long covered porch. "We'll stay here at this boarding house for a few days," Henry told them, "You ladies can rest up, and in the meantime I can get some boards out to the Homestead. We'll get a lean-to up first, Mama, then get started on our cabin. Your household crates will be here in a few days, and then we can all move right out to 'Our Homestead.'"

Oh, the ladies were so happy to put their bundles down in a clean room. The kerosene lamp was throwing nice light, and everything looked so comfy. Rosa thought the second-story room was splendid; there was even a window to look out of to see the surrounding country-side. But it made her sad to look at that. It was terrible country, all dry and bare looking. There were some green patches showing, but mostly there were those funny gray bushes all over, and lots more piles of those big, dark gray rocks. Oh my, how could anyone grow anything on this land?

Mama and Louisa slept in the bed, and Rosa had a pallet on the floor, which was fine with her. The "lavatory" was out back, but there was a big white pitcher full of water and a large bowl right in their room for "washin'-up."

Henry had told them many, many times that "Their Homestead" (Henry always made the word "Homestead" sound like a grand place and always said "Their Homestead" with great pride) was only about three miles south from the town of Springfield and also near another small town called Pingree. Rosa was hoping that maybe, way out there,

there would be a pretty green valley with a bubbly stream and some trees for shade. She figured the only thing she was going to miss about Magley would be the old apple tree. It had been her sanctuary. She called it her hidey-place. Oh, she would surely miss that ol' apple tree.

At mealtimes they got to set at a big long table with the other "boarders." They were all men except the school teacher. After a couple of days, Rosa finally got up enough courage to speak with her. She really wanted to know about the "schoolin'" in Springfield but found out very little. The schoolmarm was tall and thin. She was a very young woman, did not smile at all, and did not seem too interested in a skinny new student from Magley, Indiana.

While they were staying at the boarding house, Mama noticed that out in the back there were big piles of gunny sacks. They were probably from the stable next door. Mama kept asking around till she found out who owned those sacks; then she went over and asked if she could have some of them. Then she started right away sewing them all together with coarse twine to make a large tent-like sheet out of them. Henry was pleased and said that could be used for one side of the lean-to, and then they could use most of their boards for the cabin.

Sister Louisa had been busy, too. She found that she could help out over at the hotel dining room, so she worked over there every mealtime. Rosa spent her time walking around the small town and looking around. She went with Mama into the Mercantile to buy the twine. It was a wondrous place. There was so much to buy here, barrels of pickles and big sacks of onions and potatoes and good things in tall tins on shelves going all the way up to the ceiling. Oh, Rosa was having a grand time.

Henry had been very busy making trips out to "Their Homestead" on his trusty bicycle. One time he got a farmer's wagon to take out a good pile of logs, boards, wire, nails, and a big wired up square of alfalfa hay for a special use. Then, on the day after Mama's household crates arrived, Henry piled the ladies, all their bundles, all the crates, and other supplies onto a farm wagon. He was driving them out to "Their Home-stead."

Rosa could tell that Mama was very disappointed by the looks of the barren hills. There were some gullies and a few trees called *cotton-woods,* but there were all those gray slabs of rocks all over the land, as if a giant had just thrown them about. Henry was talking and talking about what they would do and what they could grow and seemed so happy, but the ladies were quiet.

When the wagon pulled over a little rise, Henry shouted, "Here it is; we are now on our own land. Look over there by the two cottonwood trees, Mama; there is the lean-to, and right next to that is where your cabin will be." Henry was so excited he did not notice Mama crying quietly to herself. Rosa leaned over and held her arm around Mama's shoulders.

They were all looking around at the slightly rolling land, but there was nothing, nothing but that gray sagebrush and those slabs of gray rock, just as far as the eye could see.

Rosa felt Mama's shoulders shaking, and somehow she knew exactly what Mama was thinking at the sight of this dry place. She knew Mama's heart was breaking too. What a terrible land—lonely and barren of anything pretty, just harsh and strange looking. Rosa's heart sank with despair. She wanted to cry out, to shout at Henry, "No, no, this awful place should not be Mama's new home. No, no, Henry," but she bit back the words. Even as young as Rosa was, she knew that her mama would not complain about the ugliness all around; Mama would only see this homely place as the new beginning for them all, the new beginning she had dreamed of, far from the hatred of being "those Rebels."

Mama and Louisa and Rosa all knew that this place was brother Henry's dream, a dream he had clung to and worked so hard to achieve all his life—the dream of owning his own land, his own homestead. So Mama would never say anything but praise for this place. Mama would sacrifice anything for her children's happiness.

And sure enough, Mama straightened up, still holding both girls' hands tightly, and said, "Oh my dear girls, this is our land, our very own land. It's dry and homely looking, but see, there by the trees, it looks like maybe a little creek. Oh, it is really a pretty valley, and it's our home now, our own land." And then she sighed and raised her head up to the sky, saying softly, "Oh, praise-be to this day, for this is the day the good Lord has set our feet upon this truly wonderful, new, unventured path."

CHAPTER THREE

The Homestead

AFTER THE WAGON WAS FINALLY UNLOADED, Henry had to drive it back to town to its owner and then ride his bicycle the three miles back out to the homestead. The ladies tried to get a few things arranged for the coming night. Rosa had two very important tasks to do right away. She must carry water from the stream, and she must stuff their four mattresses with the fresh straw a farmer had given Henry.

Henry brought a small sheepherder's cookstove, and before he left, he had set it up just outside the lean-to. Mama's iron cookstove was still in its crate and would be assembled later when the cabin was finished. Louisa fixed up a fast stew, and while they were eating it, poor Mama just fainted away and fell right out of her chair. The girls hurriedly got her onto her mattress and covered her with a quilt and put cool cloths on her face. She was so pale that they were frightened for her, and Henry would not be back for some time yet. But in a little while she opened her eyes and said she was all right. She guessed she was just completely tuckered-out from all the excitement. So, the girls decided that for the next few days they would try to get Mama to stay quiet on her mattress or to just set in her rocker in the shade of the lean-to.

Fortunately, sister Louisa was very adept at cooking and taking care of folks. She seemed a natural nurse and was a very good cook. Rosa was so thankful for Louisa and very, very happy that her sister had decided to come along. She did not know what they would have done without Louisa—easygoing, quiet, dependable Louisa. She was so different from Rosa. Rosa was clumsy around a stove and hated cookin' and cleanin'-up and anything that had to be done inside. But oh, how Rosa loved to haul the water and saw up the twisted branches of sagebrush for the stove. She thought that was easy compared to the cookin' and cleanin'-up chores.

On the very next day Henry told Rosa, "We must get busy, Rosa, and dig a deep hole for the privy right away. It will be fine over here." He pointed to a slight dip in the ground near an outcropping of those large lava rocks. "We'll put it here. It won't be too far from the cabin 'cause it gets mighty cold trottin' out here in winter."

The digging was tiresome, but Henry was a strong, wiry man and vigorously swung his pick and shoveled and shoveled. Then they sawed some boards and hammered a small privy all together. It had a steep, slanted roof. The doorway would open away from the cabin and look out over a slope that was studded with gray sage and slabs of rock as far as you could see, way up to the sky. "Oh, this is a fine 'lavatory,'" Rosa told Henry.

It would be Rosa's chore also to bring out the ashes from the cook stove and drop them all down the hole, but Rosa was used to this task. She had done this many, many times back in Magley. Henry had even saved an old catalog to use for paper. Mama and Louisa were very pleased with the new privy and stood around and admired Henry's and Rosa's handiwork. "I'll plant those hollyhock seeds around it," Mama told them. "It will be nice."

The very next day Henry started on the cabin. It would be small but large enough for cooking and eating and sleeping. They would not have time to put in a floor until Henry's next trip home, some months away, but no one cared. The cabin went up slowly with Henry and Rosa both sawing and holding boards and nailing it all together. They had carefully removed all the sod with the grass and pebbles from the floor area. And Rosa spent many hours smoothing and tamping down the soil to make a good hard-packed dirt floor for the time being.

The cabin seemed sturdy, especially the roof. Henry and Rosa had carefully placed the large squares of what Henry called "special roof-sod" on top of the roof boards. They just dug it up in squares down by the stream bed, with grasses and small rocks still in it, and placed it on the roof boards, one square at a time. Then Rosa had to carry many buckets of water and climb up the ladder with the heavy bucket dangling and wet down the whole roof. Then they stomped hard on it and pressed it all together so no rain could get through, so the rain would just run right off. Oh, how proud Rosa was every time she looked up at that thick sod roof; it made the cabin so cozy inside.

The day they uncrated Mama's cookstove, got it all assembled and set up, and everything settled inside the cabin, they had a special supper. Louisa had prepared a big pot of beans with bacon and molasses. It was very tasty with those fat biscuits that she knew how to make. They all felt very tired but very content. They were at last settled and had a fine roof over their heads.

Henry had to go back to his job as telegraph operator for the railroad, but before he left, he gave them all very careful instructions. Mama was to just rest up, just do the planning on what needed doing for the spring. He laughed and told her, "Now, Mama, you can catch up on all your mendin' and knittin'." Louisa was to do the cookin' and washin' as she always did. Rosa's chores would include the hauling of all the water and the sawing of all the wood for cooking. Henry had made Rosa a small sawhorse, just her size, and showed her how to lay the crooked branches of the sagebrush in the v-shaped ends so she could use her bow-saw to cut the branches into small lengths which Louisa would need for the cookstove. The sagebrush was very tough, but Rosa finally got pretty good at the sawing. She even knew how to keep her saw teeth razor sharp, just like Henry had showed her.

Also she had her own plan to start moving some rocks around in the small stream to make a deeper pool. Henry had told her that this was a real stream only in the winter and spring, but other times it was called an irrigation ditch. The water was sent down the stream bed just for the homesteaders' use, and she should not stop the flow of the water. Some of it must still go on down the stream for others to use. But he said it would be all right for her to make her own small pool to be able to dip up water with her pail.

Then there was her other task, the "jack rabbit trap." This was a very, very disagreeable task, and almost more than Rosa could bear. She and

Henry had made a neat, small, wired-in enclosure out of tightly woven chicken wire. There was one small opening in one corner of the trap. Each and every morning Rosa had to go up past the stream and check the "jack rabbit trap." There she would find one or more floppy-eared jack rabbits caught inside the trap. Each evening she would stuff a small bundle of that special alfalfa hay inside the trap. The rabbits loved alfalfa and would go inside to eat it and not be able to find their way out again. Then each morning Rosa had to carefully close off the opening and take one jack out at a time. This was no easy task, as the rabbits were wiry and almost mean, and they would get very upset at someone grabbing them by the ears. Also, they were just covered with those awful, nasty ticks, and oh, Rosa hated that.

Henry had told her that the young jacks were much more tender, but Rosa could not bring herself to keep the very young ones. She just grabbed them by the ears and set them loose outside the trap. She could tell when a mama jack was nursing young, and she would also let her go. She had the feeling that several of those mama jacks were often repeat visitors to her alfalfa.

At first Rosa carried only one rabbit at a time back to the cabin but soon became pretty good at handling two of them by the ears. She herself was so small that the jacks drug the ground, and that made them put up a bigger fight with her. This was very hard work indeed, and finally, she said to herself, "What's wrong with me, why don't I just kill the rabbits right out here by the trap, and then I won't have to fight with them all the way back to the yard, and I won't lose any this way." Rosa had become very quick with the heavy blow needed at the base of the skull to kill the rabbit immediately. She used the blunt side of her hatchet like a hammer, and it was over instantly. Back at the yard with the rabbits, she would secure the carcass to a flat board, quickly cut the skin around the neck, and in one steady pull, just yank the skin completely off the carcass. Then she would call Louisa to come out and get the skinned rabbit to complete the cleaning. Now Rosa must stretch and tack the skins of the rabbits, fur side in, on the outside of the walls of the cabin. Then she must carefully scrape away any remaining membrane and rub a salt brine mixture onto the skin. Her mama had promised to make her a rabbit-fur coat out of the skins to wear to school, and Rosa knew that if the hides were tanned just right, they would be warm and soft. She rubbed the brine into the hides extra hard and stretched the skins taut to cure just so.

Even the killing and the skinning would not have been so bad if it were not for the awful ticks the rabbits carried. After the catching and skinning were all done, Rosa had to go way down the stream, take off all her clothes, and rub her skin all over with fine sand from the stream bottom. Most days the water was very cold. She had a fine-toothed comb stashed by her bathing hole and would dip her hair up and down in the water over and over again. Then she must comb through her long brown hair to make sure all the ticks were washed away before she could plait it up again into one long braid. Then she had to wash and dip her skirt and shirtwaist and stockings up and down in the water and lay them on a rock for the sun to dry, and put on the dry clothes which had been washed the same way the day before. Rosa laughed to herself about that. If she did not have two skirts and two waists, she guessed she would have to wear a sagebrush dress.

Even if this was her most disagreeable chore, Rosa felt proud of being able to do her part. Mama and Louisa were so very pleased with this never ending supply of fresh meat and always praised Rosa for her splendid "jack rabbit trap."

Sister Louisa became very good at stewing up the rabbits with different herbs and greens. She knew how to pick wild things that were good to eat, and she was always trying out something new. Even here in a very different land, she seemed to know what was good to eat. She even breaded pieces of the young rabbits and cooked them in her huge iron pot with bacon grease till they were all brown and crusty, and that was Rosa's favorite.

One day a neighbor came by with his wagon and team. He said he lived over yonder 'bout a mile, and he brought them a fine sack of potatoes. He told the ladies, "Until you get your own crop in, you just bring over a sack and you dig up all the potatoes you need in my fields, and there are some cabbages and turnips from last year stored down in my root cellar that will surely go bad if someone don't eat 'em." So Rosa made many trips over the hill and came back dragging her sack full of potatoes and turnips and cabbages. Several times, the farmer's wife sent her home with some real dried apples, and Louisa quickly whipped up a dried apple pie, and that was Mama's favorite treat in the whole world.

Even as hard as they all worked, from dawn till dusk, all three of them started to look better and feel better. Rosa's skinny frame filled out some in spite of the hard manual labor she was doing all day long. Many nights during her prayers, Rosa would politely ask the Lord to help her grow a bit faster. She was a tiny girl for her age, skinny and wiry, but very strong. She would pray, "Dear Lord, please help me to get some bigger so when I do go to the new school this fall, no one will ever, ever, ever again call me 'Skinny Scotty, the Rebel Brat.'"

When brother Henry came home again, there was so much to tell him and so much for him to see. He was very pleased at how "Their Homestead" was starting to look. Every evening was filled with plans and discussions of the work. Henry had arrived with another wagon loaded with all sorts of necessities. Planks for the floor of the cabin, seed potatoes, grain seed, vegetable seed, some real tea for Mama, beans and sugar and salt, a small milk cow, four very upset Rhode Island red hens, and one large squawking rooster.

Henry arranged for a neighbor to bring his work team with a big harrow like thing, and they spent days dragging it back and forth across a large patch of sagebrush. The wiry sagebrush just came out by the roots and was dragged up into big rows around the field. They had to try to move all of the smaller rocks out of the field also. Then they plowed up the soil and disked it down to prepare it for the planting. All this was done in the two weeks Henry had off from his work. The ladies planted potatoes, with all the eyes up of course, broadcast the grain, and planted all the seeds in the garden. The garden had to be tightly fenced in because of the rabbits and other wild things that would surely love the new growth.

One day Henry took Rosa up on the slope where the ditch ran, and they plotted where they would start digging their own small irrigation ditch. It would run from the main stream down across a slope and right into the vegetable garden. They carefully planned how the water would run down by its own gravity, and Rosa even enjoyed the digging. Oh, it was certainly a thrill to finally let the water seek its way down their small ditch and flood the neat garden rows.

Before Henry left again, he explained to Rosa just how they would dig a root cellar later on. He told her, "You can start if you want, Rosa, but this is hard man's work, so if it is too hard for you, let it go till I get back." He staked the thing out and showed her just how wide and how deep they would make it. They would use flat stones for steps leading down into the cellar. "Maybe you can be on the look out, Rosa, for some nice, big, flat ones we can use for the floor. Remember where they are so I can move them when I get back; then we will put the roof on the root cellar and cover it with sod, just like we did on the cabin."

The first evening after Henry had left, while the ladies were having their supper, Rosa decided she would ask Mama about something that had been on her mind for some time. "Mama, I want to ask you, well, to ask if it would be alright if I could have a pair of britches like boys wear. Oh, I know you always tell me I have to act ladylike, but Mama, when Henry is away, I am the man here, I do the outside chores. Oh, I like to do the outside chores, but Mama, a long skirt is just always getting caught on something. It's in the way of my tasks, and you know how many times you have had to mend my skirts for me. Maybe you could stitch up a pair of britches for me out of that wool you have. I could do my work so much easier, Mama. I have to dig a root cellar, and it's so hard to dig in a skirt." Finally she ran out of breath and just looked at her Mama solemnly, waiting for the answer she was so afraid to hear.

Well, her Mama broke right out in a laugh and Louisa joined in; they laughed and laughed. Then Mama said, "Oh little Rosey, my dear little Rosey, I know you can't be ladylike when you're sawin' and diggin' and trappin' rabbits, but trousers, britches on my little girl? Oh Rosey girl, what an idea." But then she looked at Rosa's face and was quiet for a long while, and then she said, "Rosey, I tell you what we'll do, we will just make you a pair of those britches and you can do your work in them, but soon as you see a neighbor coming along, you run and hide. I will not have anyone around here making fun of my little girl for wearing britches. Can you promise me that, Rosa Ellen?"

Well, it did not take her mama very long to stitch up a pair of black wool britches for Rosa. Rosa said they were very fine indeed, and it was oh so easy to bend over in them. She felt completely free whenever she wore them, which was every day. She loved to run and jump as high as she could. Oh, it was a wonder to be able to do that. Boys really have it better than girls, she thought, they surely do.

Rosa loved checking the water ditch. She carried the big hoe slung over her small shoulder and used it to clean out any debris that might hamper the flow of water in her irrigation ditch. She was always finding new ways to divert any extra water out onto the grain and potato fields. Of course her chores now included milking ol' mama cow, morning and evening, feeding the chickens, gathering eggs, and making sure all the hens were tightly penned in for the night. There were many night varmints that would surely love to eat a fat hen. But she always had to be on the lookout for the big red rooster. Somehow he had taken a dislike to Rosa, or maybe he just didn't like anyone. He would run at her from behind and peck at her ankles something fierce. She tried to remember to carry a switch with her, but sometimes when she forgot, she had to "run like the dickens" to get away from his angry pecking.

There was the wild grass for the cow, but she did tend to wander, so Rosa must keep an eye out for her many times during the day. She still hauled all the water, chopped and sawed up the sagebrush for the stove, and still had to tend the rabbit trap, then take her morning bath in the ditch to rid herself of the awful ticks. Soon that too became just another chore because they must have the rabbits for food, and difficult as it was, she was happy she could help out in this way.

Now there was the digging of the root cellar to consider. Rosa had made up her mind that she would dig it herself before Henry came home again. She could do it, just a little at a time. And it did take her all the months till it was about time for school to start. It was slow work, especially when she would run into a lot of river rocks and stones. At night she would plan in her head just how she would, step by step, complete the cellar which Henry had planned. When she got down deeper than her head, it was very tiresome lifting bucket after bucket of soil up the short ladder, to be dumped and spread out. Then she was so proud of the perfect flat stones she had found and carefully fitted together to make steps leading down into her cellar. They were so grand that she kept searching till she found enough flat stones that were not too heavy, and she fitted them all together kind of like a crazy quilt to make a floor for the cellar. She fitted thick sod in between the stones and wet it down and stomped on it so that there was a nice flat floor. Mama and Louisa tried out her steps and walked on her cellar floor and were very proud of Rosa. "Oh little sweetheart," her Mama said when she hugged her, "I guess you should have been a boy; you surely think like a boy, and you surely work like a boy, and you have built a truly fine root cellar."

Now Rosa turned her mind to the roof for her root cellar. Oh, this would be easy compared to the digging. She placed the boards Henry had said were for the roof and then placed squares of sod she dug up and lugged over to her cellar in the wheelbarrow. She was still cutting and laying the last of the sod when Henry arrived home.

When she showed her work to Henry, he grabbed her hands and danced her around till she was dizzy. He was singing, "Rosa made a root cellar; Rosa made a fine root cellar all by herself, fancy stone steps and even a handsome roof. Rosa is a clever girl; Rosa made us a root cellar." Louisa and Mama came out and laughed with them. When a neighbor came by one day, Henry proudly escorted him down into "Rosa's root cellar." Oh, Rosa was so proud and happy that she had done this big chore for "The Homestead." Rosa's root cellar would be there for a long, long time, maybe forever.

Rosa always felt a great rush of joy inside when she finished up some task for the good of the Homestead. This was their home, their land, and if she could do something, no matter how hard the work or how long it would take, she would do it, and then she would feel that great satisfaction when it was all done. Her joy came in knowing that this was for Mama and Henry and Louisa and for their "Homestead." Yes, Rosa's root cellar was a fine task, well done, and her root cellar would be there forever and ever.

It was September of 1905, and time for Rosa to start school again. Now she had missed almost a whole year of schooling, but Mama told her, "Because you started early to school, you can catch up easily, Rosa. You are very smart and a very clever girl, and you will not have any trouble at all."

Rosa kept thinking about her mama saying she was "very smart and a very clever girl," and that made her feel good, but she was a little scared. She was pretty friendly with the three small boys of the neighboring farm, so she would walk over to their place and walk the other two miles into Springfield with them. Her sister Louisa had never gone to school very much. She knew how to read and write though, mostly from Mama's teachings, and Louisa always encouraged Rosa to learn as much as she could and study real hard.

It was the same unsmiling school teacher she had met early in the spring at the boarding house. Schoolin' was very serious for Miss June Stanton, and she would not tolerate any wandering mind. She was quick

42

with her ruler, and it snapped the back of a hand often when anyone was being unruly or not paying close attention.

Rosa was shy among so many children, but she was also very serious about her learnin'. If her mama thought she was a clever, smart girl, she would study real hard and catch up to her grade. She read her lessons over and over and recited them over and over on her long walk home. Then each evening she would recite what she had learned to Mama and Louisa.

Being the new girl in the school, she had to put up with some cutting words from a few of the bully-boys that were always mean to everyone, but no one called her Skinny Scotty; not once did anyone call her Skinny Scotty. She thanked the good Lord for that miracle every day on her walk home. What a big relief not to be called that anymore.

But there was another problem, and it seemed that this one was not going away. As Rosa grew, her teeth seemed to grow too but much too fast; they were getting larger and larger. She was not aware of this, as she never looked in any mirror. She also had a decided overbite and, of course, took a lot of teasing about "bucky-teeth" or having a "squirrely face." If her teeth had not been so pronounced, Rosa would have been a very beautiful little girl. She had soft, light brown hair, a lovely peaches-and-cream skin, tanned by the sun, and the most incredible sky-blue eyes that danced all the time. Oh well, she decided, at least no one calls me "Rebel Brat" with hatefulness, and no one calls me "Skinny Scotty" either, so that is a whole lot to be thankful for.

By this time the fall harvesting was beginning, and the ladies were busier than ever. The garden had done fairly well, even though there seemed to be as many pests eating up everything here as there had been in Indiana, just different kinds. There were many large green grasshoppers and funny looking gray worms. The gophers were also a menace to everything. But Rosa was sure that the garden was producing enough for all the pests and also enough to harvest for the family because of her careful tending of the water flow. That had to be watched daily, but she did so enjoy playing with the water and making sure her ditches were clean and flowing nicely. Besides, with all her outside chores to do, she did not have to "help out" with all the weedin' of the garden and the cookin' and cannin', and that suited her just fine.

Now that the hard work of digging the root cellar was over, Rosa must concentrate on the winter supply of firewood. Mama's big, old, black iron cookstove would keep them nice and warm, and it was good to smell the big kettle of soup simmering on the back of the stove every day. Louisa surely knew how to make wonderful vittles, and she often told Rosa how very nice it was to go down into "Rosa's root cellar" and pick out what she needed for supper. Rosa was so proud of her cellar that she even carved her name into the top board of the heavy wooden door that Henry had made for her cellar. Oh, that was so much fun. But Rosa was also proud of the neat stacks of wood she cut and piled up around the outside of the cabin walls.

Mama had been sorting and cutting the rabbit skins they had, and when she figured she had enough, she started to make the coat for Rosa. She told her with a smile, "Rosey, it's a good thing I didn't start cutting this coat out earlier, because you're growin' so fast it would be way too small. Why, you're growin' just like those weeds out there in the garden."

Rosa loved to hear her Mama say such a nice thing about her, but she wasn't so sure she was growin' that fast; her arms and legs still looked awful scrawny to her. Rosa would always be a small girl. Even as a grown woman, she was only five feet three inches tall, and not until very late in her life did she ever weigh over ninety pounds. But she must have been like a wiry whip and very strong to do such difficult, back-breaking labor at the age of nine—actually the work of a full grown man.

Indeed, it was a struggle the first years on the Homestead. But there was enough to eat, thanks to the jack rabbits, the neighbors' extra potatoes and cabbages, and Henry's monthly letters containing enough money for the necessities.

Fortunately, Mama was very clever with her knitting, and with what wool she had brought with her, she was able to knit up mufflers and gloves that were traded to some of the neighbors for other supplies. Her Mama did not mind this work at all; she always told Louisa and Rosa that she could knit all day and never get tuckered-out. Rosa knew that her Mama was feeling better because she did not have to do washin' every day out in the cold like she used to back in Magley. Oh, Rosa was happy for that, and every morning when she awakened, she would thank the Lord that they were in Idaho and not in Magley, Indiana.

Each Saturday night, rain or shine or storm or cold, it was bath night. Mama had brought her big tin wash tub, of course. She had told the girls,

44

"Why, this is the very same tub that I used when I was a girl. It surely has seen a lot of scrubbin'." The tub was dented and old and gray, but big enough for even a lady to sit in in comfort and plenty big enough for Rosa. Louisa always heated up three big kettlefulls of hot water and also used hot water from the water well in the big cookstove. This called for many, many buckets of water to be hauled in from the stream. There was the harsh homemade soap that smelled so strongly of lye. The ladies took turns, Mama always first, then Louisa, then Rosa, with some water dipped out and more hot water added each time. Mama would always laugh and tell Rosa, "Now Rosey, you wash everything as far down as possible, then you wash everything as far up as possible, and then you wash that possible."

CHAPTER FOUR

The Kit-Horse

HIS SAME YEAR OF 1905, on October 29th, it would be Rosa's tenth birthday. Oh, she was looking forward to that. She was sure that brother Henry would be home for a few days, and Mama had made plans for the neighboring family to come over for the noonday meal on Sunday for a small celebration. Oh, it was going to be a wonderful day, and Rosa counted the weeks.

Finally, the day of her birthday arrived. Louisa and Mama were preparing a very nice meal, and Rosa was finishing up her chores in the cool, clear morning. She was still out by the wood pile when she saw a wagon coming at a good clip down their lane. There was a small horse tied up behind the wagon, just trotting along, the black mane and tail flying in the wind. "Why, that's Henry," Rosa said. She called out to him, "Henry, oh Henry, you did come for my birthday! Hello there, Henry." She ran to meet him as he drew up the team beside the cabin.

"Rosa Ellen!" he shouted to her, "Come here, Rosey; I have your special birthday present from Uncle Albert. Look here, Rosa, you now have a sweet little horse all your very own."

"Oh no." Rosa suddenly stopped running and just stood there numb, thinking, "A horse all my own, a real saddle horse. Oh, Uncle Albert said he would do this, but I never dreamed, I never ever thought I would have my own horse. Oh, this is just a dream; it is not so." She closed her eyes for a few seconds and just stood there, then she opened them up fast and wide. Yes, there was Henry getting down from the wagon, and there was a small golden horse tied up to the back of the wagon, so maybe it was not a dream after all. Her legs started shaking, and she could hardly move. Somehow she got over to Henry and hugged his lanky frame. "Oh Henry, is this so? Is this my very own horse? Did Uncle Albert send me such a grand present as this?"

Henry took her hand and walked her to the back of the wagon saying, "Yes, Rosey, Uncle Albert sent me the money, and I found this special horse just for you. She was a real wild mustang, Rosa, but now she is very tame. Some cowboys started to break her, but they decided she would never grow big enough to work on a cattle ranch, so they decided to sell her. Her name is Kit because she is so small, I guess. They call her a buckskin because her coat is honey colored. See that brown stripe down her back and the black tail? That there is a real buckskin-mustang, Rosa. They say that a buckskin has a rebel coat, tough and mean. Well, we ain't rebels no more, Rosey, and you can be proud of this one's 'rebel coat.' And you know what, Rosey? They told me that this mare is a natural born single-footer; just like ridin' in a rockin' chair they say. Well, little sister, what do you think of her?"

Tears of joy were streaming down Rosa's cheeks; she could not speak. She just held out her hand, walking very slowly up to the horse, whispering softly, "Nice little horse, nice Kit, you are really and truly my very own horse now, and, and I hope you will like me. I think you are so beautiful; you are such a beautiful little Kit-horse."

The small, black muzzle moved forward to smell Rosa's out-stretched palm, and the horse snorted softly, pushing gently against Rosa's small hand. Oh, Rosa was so excited! There were big fat butter-flies churning in her tummy. Oh, oh, her very own horse! She carefully patted the sleek neck and then slowly put both arms around Kit's neck, talking to her gently. Then she just held the little horse and cried and sobbed with her cheek leaning against the soft, living warmth.

This was the most splendid thing that had ever ever happened to her. This was her very own horse, her Kit, her own saddle-horse, her own pretty little Kit-horse. She felt as if her heart would just burst right out of her chest. She was feeling dizzy and funny all at once, so she just clung to the little horse.

Mama and Louisa had come out of the cabin and were welcoming Henry. They all looked at Rosa with her arms wrapped around the little horse. Henry smiled broadly, and Mama and Louisa wiped tears away with their white aprons.

After a while, Henry came over and patted Rosa's shoulder. "Now, now, Rosey, yes, little sister, this is your very own horse, but you know, we better get her over to the water trough. She'll be thirsty, I know. Here, you can just lead her over with the lead rope. See, she is a well mannered little mare."

Rosa led her horse to the water and watched in fascination as the horse softly dipped her small black muzzle into the cool water. She drank deeply and then splashed the water back and forth as if to say, "Thank you, Rosa, this is very good water indeed." And Rosa laughed through her tears.

The rest of that day, and for months and months, Rosa was in a deep trance. She could think of nothing but her "Kit-horse." She kept looking at her every chance she could, and petting her and grooming her and feeding her. Rosa had a lot of trouble getting her chores done now, and going off to school was torture. She would run most of the way home and down the lane to see the little horse.

For the next week, every day after school, Henry taught her how to care for Kit, and she listened very, very carefully to everything he told her about horses—how to groom them, how to feed them. She learned how to run her hand slowly down along Kit's chest and withers and to gently pick up each small hoof, to use the small knife and carefully dig out any tiny pebbles that might hurt the horse when it walked. There was no saddle, but Henry said that riding bareback was the best way to really learn to ride. "You can feel the horse under you, and that's the only way to learn proper. Now Rosey, I guess you're ready to ride this here Kit-horse."

To actually be sitting on Kit and walking her around the yard was pure bliss for Rosa. She quickly learned how to neck rein her, as this was the way the cowboys had trained her. Henry told her, "This horse was trained with a hackamore, Rosey. It's really easier on a horse than a bridle with a bit. See, this large rawhide knot under her chin is where she feels your pull from the reins. You see, cowboys need their horses to stop fast and turn fast, so you just lay the reins against the side of her neck, and she will turn the opposite way. That's called neck-reinin'. Hold the reins in just one hand, now turn the reins the way you want to go; see how easy she turns? But be very careful though; if she's running and you do that, she will turn so fast that you will fly right off her. She will turn, but you'll go straight and take a tumble. 'Course a horse gets to know you pretty soon, and then you can almost guide her with some pressure on her with your knees. She is right smart, Rosey." And he laughed when he said, "And Rosey, I'll bet she will teach you a thing or two, little sister."

Now, of course, there was never enough daylight for Rosa. She hurried through her chores and almost ran the three miles to and from school every day. At dark, her mama had to call her. "Put Kit away now, Rosa, time for supper and lessons."

This was the beginning of a long, true love affair. The little horse would nicker so happily when Rosa ran out of the cabin every morning. Kit would trot over to the gate and wait for Rosa to come and pet her and feed her. Henry and Rosa had built a fence around a good size chunk of land for Kit and ol' Cow so they could graze and not get lost. But Rosa had to cut wild grass everyday and stuff it into the small barn that she and Henry had also built. There would not be anything to graze on in winter, and the animals must be fed. Evidently Uncle Albert had sent Henry enough for the horse and to pay for a barn and to buy extra winter feed too, and Rosa had written Uncle Albert a six-page letter thanking him and telling him how splendid this birthday gift of her Kit-horse was.

The day soon arrived when Mama said Rosa was ready to ride Kit to and from school. Many boys rode horses to school, and although several girls rode double behind their brothers, there were no other girls riding their very own horse like Rosa would be doing. There was a small corral behind the schoolhouse for the horses during the school day. Rosa planned to take a small sack of grain for her horse to be fed at noon-time. Mama had sewn up two small, flat bags out of old, soft leather that would be slung over like saddlebags in front of Rosa as she rode. There was room for the grain for Kit and for Rosa's noon-time food and her one small notebook that she always carried. This was no trouble at all for Rosa; the bags rode there very easily.

There never was a prouder day in all of Rosa's life than when that day came. She trotted her sweet little buckskin right down the lane to the schoolhouse. Everyone, all the children, and even Miss Stanton, stared open-mouthed at Rosa and that pretty little Kit-horse.

The children looked over her horse very carefully, and a few said what a fine riding horse she had there. Even though some of the boys made remarks about a broom-tailed Indian pony, a girl riding all by herself like she was somethin', and other hateful things, Rosa knew they were all very envious of this small buckskin horse.

From then on Rosa rode Kit to school as proud as could be. She learned to roll with Kit's single-footed gait. Kit's right front leg and her right back leg would be picked up and moved together, then the left front and left back leg would follow in a rocking motion. For some mustangs this was not an unusual gait, but very few breeds of horses had what some called the rack. This seemed very natural for Kit, and it certainly was like riding a rocking chair, smooth and easy with no jolting trot like other horses. Kit could not go along very fast, but she could keep up this rolling gait for hours at a time and never seem to tire. When she was on her Kit-horse, Rosa felt like the Queen of England, and she would sing to herself, "I am the Queen, I am the Queen of I-de-ho."

Now it seemed that Rosa's whole life was different, just different than it ever was before; she could feel the change in herself and often pondered on it. Somehow, she did not feel shy with anyone anymore. She held her head higher, she walked prouder, she felt stronger, as if she could do just about anything. She was Rosa Ellen Scott, she was ten years old, and she would always be riding her very own buckskin with the rebel coat, her own Kit-horse.

All during the fall days and the harvesting seasons for the farmers around the area, Mama and Louisa were hiring-out. The farmers were so happy to get someone with Mama's skills at butchering and making her famous head-cheese and blood sausages, and curing all the bacons and hams so tastefully. They would come over in their wagons and pick up Mama and Louisa, and the two of them would be gone for a few days at each farm.

Rosa was not a bit afraid to be left all alone; she never even gave it a second thought. She was very independent and enjoyed the time by herself; she and Kit were never alone. Of course she hated cookin' anything, so Louisa always left her a big pot of soup that she could just heat up every evening. Louisa often told her, "Rosa Ellen, I do declare, you will just have to learn to cook sometime. Someday you will have a husband and children; then what are you goin' to do to feed all those hungry mouths?" Then she would laugh and just fix up something tasty to leave on the back of the stove for Rosa to eat while they were gone.

When the weather started to be very bitter and cold, Rosa decided to have another talk with Mama about britches. "You see, Mama, it is very cold riding to school. I could wear some britches under my long skirt and stuff them inside my boots. No one will ever know they are under there. They will be just like the long black stockings all the girls wear under skirts. Please, Mama, a pair of britches, rabbit-skin trousers would be so warm on my legs, and I could get my outside chores done lickety-split 'cause I could just take off my skirt when I first get home and then get right to my work." She knew this time it was going to be tough convincing Mama, so she hurried on to tell her, "And I could go to school even in blizzards or any kind of weather, Mama. I will wear the lace-up boots and slicker that Henry brought for me and never be cold for a minute. Kit gets me home in such a hurry, I will never miss a day of school, all dressed up so warm in rabbit-skin britches and coat."

Well, Rosa did get a new pair of britches sewn up. The warm rabbit fur was cozy with the fur turned inside, and even with the long woolen skirt over the britches, she felt free; oh, she felt really free. But she must keep the skirt tucked in around her legs when she was nearing the school. Mama did not want her Rosey to be called a girl who wore britches like a boy.

On Sundays, after morning chores, Mama would set in her rocker and read aloud from the Bible. "Someday," she would say, "we will have a wagon and drive over to the church, but now we must honor the Lord's Day by reading from his Word."

Rosa's mother, Mary Catherine, was a fairly well educated woman. Her mother, Rosa's grandmother, had immigrated from Ireland as a young woman, and she had been schooled in Ireland. She taught her children to read and write and do sums. In turn, Mary Catherine made sure that all her children, all eight of them that lived, could also read and write and do simple sums. She was able to help them all "do their lessons" when it was too cold for them to go to school, or if they had to stay home and work, she would help them in the evenings. She said she wanted to make sure that all her children had "learnin'."

In Idaho, winters set in early, and it became cold and blustery. The ladies often talked about how the wind blew the rain and snow right across the countryside, not straight down like respectable rain should fall. Well, at least Rosa was happy about one thing: with the cold weather here, the jack rabbits didn't seem to have many ticks on them, and it was much too cold to bathe in the creek anymore. So Louisa always set a basin of warm water in the lean-to for Rosa. Having run out of alfalfa,

Rosa was now using what turnip leaves and old carrot tops and such that were left over from the garden. These had carefully been saved in "Rosa's root cellar" for just this purpose. Oh, how the jacks loved this change of diet; Rosa always found two or three long-earred jacks in her trap.

Now that winter was here, Rosa became worried that there would not be enough wild hay stored up to feed ol' Cow, and also her Kit-horse, till spring. She knew the grazing would be very sparse during the winter. She wrote and told Henry about her concern and received this reply:

My dear little sister Rosey,

Don't you worry none, I will bring a good load of hay and grain on my Christmas visit home. It's good of you to think about this but you see, you and I are partners, Rosey, you have done a very good job of being the man of the homestead for me. I will make sure your Kit gets plenty of hay for the winter. You know that we partners always work together and I am very proud of all the work my partner does on Our Homestead.

Rosa puffed with pride at these words coming from big brother Henry. She worshiped brother Henry and had a great deal of respect for him, and now he said they were real partners. She tucked the letter in a tin box with her few other treasures and often read it over and would feel the warmth of pride each time she read it.

Rosa liked her school time and was fast becoming an admirer of her teacher, Miss June Stanton. Miss Stanton had introduced the children to poetry, and Rosa read everything that she had available. There were not many books in the school, and they had to be handled with care and wrapped up carefully if taken home so as not to get wet or damaged in any way. There was one part of a poem that Rosa memorized because she loved it so. It was by the great poet Henry Wadsworth Longfellow and called "Prelude." This seemed to fit Rosa's mood each time she went up on the highest slope behind the cabin. There were great slabs of lava rock scattered all about, just like they had been strewn there by a mighty hand. One favorite flat stone was now her hidey-place. She loved to sit there whenever she could. She watched the sky and the sage slopes that receded far away into the purple distance. Sometimes, she could see the faraway rounded cones of two mountains sticking up into the sky, and they always looked very lonely way out there. When she saw these mountains with a few fluffy clouds drifting over their tops, she would recite aloud:

And dreams of that which cannot die,
Bright visions, came to me,
As lapped in thought I used to lie,
And gaze into the summer sky,
Where the sailing clouds went by,
Like ships upon the sea.

CHAPTER FIVE

Mama's Stories

NOW THE DAYS WERE GETTING SHORTER; darkness set in very early so Rosa had to hurry through her chores, get Kit brushed, and hurry inside for her supper. Then she must do her lessons.

Sometimes, during the long winter evenings, she would get Mama to tell a story. They would turn the kerosene lamp way down low to save fuel, and the three ladies would pull their chairs round the old cook stove for warmth. Mama would set in her rocking chair with her shawl around her and tell them about her own childhood. Usually she told about growing up on the big farm her papa and mama had in Indiana.

But Rosa's most favorite story was about her own grandmama, Clarissa Bristol, and how she came to America on a big boat. Clarissa was an only child of an elderly couple living in Dublin, Ireland. Her parents owned a small tailoring shop. Elizabeth, Clarissa's mother, died when Clarissa was only ten years old. So she took over her mother's duties, cooked, cleaned, and also worked in the tailoring shop with her father. Her mother had taught Clarissa how to sew, and she was a very fine seamstress. Her father was the tailor, and they worked long hours together in the shop. When Clarissa was fifteen, her father died, and then and there, Clarissa made up her mind that she was going to America. She made arrangements to sell what she could and had enough for her fare on the boat. It was unheard of for a young girl of fifteen to go to America alone, but she was determined that nothing, or no one, was going to stop her. She had to fib about her age— well, it was more like a lie than a fib, but she looked older. She was dressed very elegantly and ladylike, as she knew how to copy the very latest styles. She even convinced the authorities that she had family in America who would look after her as soon as she arrived.

When the ship left the harbor she was so happy to be on board. She was going to America, to a new life. She did not feel the least bit afraid. She knew she could make her own way. Clarissa was very adventurous and explored the ship. Of course she was not supposed to go up onto the second or first class decks, but somehow she found a way to walk around these decks, too. As she was an accomplished dressmaker, she always wore the finest designed gowns, so she was not out of place, even on the first class deck. One lady asked Clarissa about her beautifully stitched shirtwaist with all the ribbons running through the many tucks. This was the beginning of many orders for similar shirtwaists from the ladies in first class passage. Clarissa had been smart to bring along some bolts of fine Irish linen in her steamer trunks, so she made herself some extra funds all during the voyage.

Most of the time, even when the weather was cold, she would sit out on the deck in a quiet spot and stitch. She only had one small bunk in a dark corner with many other women, so it was impossible to sew down in steerage where they had been quartered.

Several times she was aware of a large, blond, young man gazing her way. He is a farmer for sure, she thought, with that heavy, hand-woven shirt and those sturdy boots. He has a serious face; he looks nice and sort of lost, but then, I guess we are all on an adventuresome journey. We are all just a little afraid of what will happen to us in America.

No wonder the big, blond, young man kept staring at Clarissa. She must have made a pretty picture, sitting there in her lovely shirtwaist and colorful shawl, with the sunlight playing on her auburn hair, just stitching away, so unconcerned with anything around her.

He finally got up the courage to speak to her and ask if there was anyone using the chair next to her. She looked up at him and smiled, and his heart turned over. Oh, he was so proud that he had learned to speak some English. Her Irish was lilting and sweet, and he had never heard anything so beautiful before. Even though he could not quite understand her words, that first smile said it was alright for him to sit.

She learned that he was John William Miller and that he was German and that he was going to America to get some of that homestead land. As they slowly became acquainted, she realized that this was a good, honest, kind-hearted man. He had left Germany, as he was all alone too, without family anymore. He said he wanted his own land, some of that fine new land that America was givin' away.

The ship sailed into New York Harbor through a heavy mist. Standing on the deck among all the other immigrants, all trying to catch a glimpse of the promised land, John took Clarissa's hand and asked her to marry him, and she said "Yes."

They finally landed at the Immigration Center, called Castle-Garden, which was located at the Battery on the southern tip of Manhattan Island. Then during the long days of getting through the immigration processes, John inquired around until he found a preacher who could marry them. He had told Clarissa that he was a good farmer, a good blacksmith, that he would care for her always, and that he would build her a fine home on his new homestead land.

They were soon on their way out of the city of New York, heading west. John had enough savings to buy a cart and oxen, and they traveled with many other immigrants also going west. John was indeed a fine blacksmith and had his tools with him. He made a good living repairing wagon wheels and shoeing oxen and horses as they traveled.

When they reached Indiana, they decided to homestead there. Over the years, John William did build Clarissa a sturdy log home, and they were very content together. They raised two boys and a girl. John was the oldest son, then Albert, then Mary Catherine. As the years went by, the farm flourished, and it was a good life for the family. Clarissa made sure her children could read and write and do simple sums.

As the two boys reached sixteen and seventeen, they began hearing about the big gold rush in Californy. They became more and more sure that they could make their fortune easily in the gold fields. As much as their father tried to dissuade them, they both decided to start out for the West. They would go together, and they would walk with their packs on their backs. They were strapping young men, big and fine looking and eager for adventure.

Clarissa said it was the saddest day of her life when she had to say good-by to her two sons. Father John William was completely devastated on losing the pride of his life, his boys who were going to take over

56

his farm someday. There must have been some heated arguments for many months before their leaving.

After the boys left the farm, nothing went well. John William worked very hard, and one day he had a serious accident. Somehow a tree fell on him and crushed one of his legs. In time he managed to walk again, but he had to use a heavy cane to help along the damaged leg. Also during these hard times for the family, the Civil War was threatening the whole country.

Everyone felt the ravages of the war. Clarissa often said, "I never thought I would be glad my boys left Indiana and the East, but I am now, else they would have been caught up in this ugly fight. I'm glad they are way out West."

Many times there would be troops marching proudly along the road near the family farm. But after the war was over, they just straggled by in small, sad groups. Many of these men were in need of food and water and medical attention. Clarissa and her daughter Mary Catherine would hurry down their lane with whatever food they had to give to these poor men. Clarissa would say, "How can we help them all? So many, so young, but we will try. Even if it's weak soup, we must try to give them some solace." And often they would take in a young man who was in need of doctoring and just could not travel any further. They always nursed them as best they could and fed them until they were able to go on their way. Three of these soldiers they could not help, and they prayed for their souls and buried them out near a small stand of trees behind the pasture.

One tall, slender soldier who they nursed back to health stayed on when he got better. He helped as best he could around the farm as he regained his strength. Then in a very short time, James Henry Scott and Mary Catherine were married and continued to live on at the farm. Clarissa was very happy they did because John William was failing each and every day.

Then, as fate would have it, six months after the marriage of Mary and James, Mama Clarissa died of a fever that was sweeping the country. John William lost his will to live after losing his beloved little Irish lass and passed away shortly after that.

Now Mary Catherine and James Henry must work the farm, and it seemed that everything that *could* go wrong did go wrong for them. James was really not a farmer; he knew nothing about crops and such. He was well educated but certainly not adept at fixing anything. He also was not very well, evidently suffering from a lung disease.

They did struggle on for many years with the farm, probably going into debt every year. Mary Catherine gave birth to a child almost every other year, and just after the birth of her seventh child, the farmhouse burnt to the ground. Fortunately everyone was safe, but they had to live in the barn with only what they were wearing. Somehow there was not the usual help from the neighboring farmers. Even though all the neighbors had had great respect for John William and Clarissa, they all felt that the new owner of the farm, James Henry Scott, was one of those hated "Rebels," and they would not have anything to do with him or his family.

They finally had to sell out, and evidently they had enough to buy a small home on a few acres near Magley, Indiana. That is where Rosa Ellen was born, the youngest of the ten children. In 1899, when Rosa was four, her father, James Henry, died.

Mama Mary's stories did not dwell long on those sad times for her family. She would mostly tell of the happy times when she was young and the apple of her two older brothers' eyes. She would talk about the children's papa, James Henry, how kind and gentle he was, how intelligent and educated. And she would tell about the birth of her children. "You know, Rosa," she always told her, "when you were born, and all the other children gathered round to take a look at their new sister, one of your big brothers said, 'Look at that little pinched up prune-face; what a funny lookin' baby, Mama.' And you know what I told them? 'Oh no, she is so sweet; look, she looks just like a tiny, pink rose-bud, just starting to open up, and someday she will be the loveliest rose of all, so we will call her Rose,' and that's how you got your name, Rosa Ellen."

CHAPTER SIX

Growing Up

URING THE NEXT YEARS Rosa was a happy girl. She did fill out a little as she had prayed she would. She was still a very small girl, but somehow this did not bother her at all anymore. She rode her "Kit-horse" to school, into town for supplies, and to the neighboring farms, and felt she was the queen of her whole universe. She and the little horse were always together, and everyone came to know Rosa and her single-footing "Kit-horse." Most everyone was friendly and spoke to Rosa, and no one, not one person, ever called her "Skinny Scotty, the Rebel Brat," either.

But Rosa had one little problem. She was still having trouble with some of the older boys in school, and now some of the older boys in town, too. They seemed to take great pleasure in cruelly taunting her. Most of the time she just ignored them. She knew she could hold her own, but a few times she got into serious, rough-and-tumble fisticuffs, which caused her some very, very serious problems with her teacher and definitely with Mama. "Oh, Rosa Ellen," Mama would sigh, "why do you have to fight? That is just not ladylike at all. Now, I do not want to hear of that anymore, Rosa Ellen; ladies do not resort to that kind of thing."

One time Henry brought home a wagon, pulled by two sturdy plowhorses. He was so proud that now the Homestead would have work-horses, and Mama would have a wagon to ride to church. It was a special time for all of them. He even brought new boards and shingles for a new roof for the cabin, and they built a sleeping loft up there for Rosa and Louisa, which was grand.

Without Henry's job on the railroad, there would have been no way for the Homestead to flourish or even survive. But Henry was working hard toward his dream of someday being able to quit his job and work full time on his own land, his Homestead. He had great plans that someday it would be a fine farm with all the land cultivated and producing. Henry scrimped and saved every penny he could for this dream. He lived at the train station, slept on a cot in the back room, and sometimes worked shifts of twenty-four to forty-eight hours at a time in order to get time off to get out to the Homestead.

Then, during the next two years, there was a terrible drought, the rains never came, and not much of any crop survived the second year. The garden was very poor indeed, as the irrigation water all but dried up. There was not much water for the stock and very little for household use. It was a very hard time for them and for all the other farmers in the whole state.

One day Henry came home and said they had to find water or all would be lost. Without water they would have to move off the Homestead. They must put down a well, even if it meant going heavily in debt. He found a man called a water-witcher, a diviner, and brought him out to the Homestead. His name was Witherspoon.

Early one morning, Henry and Mr. Witherspoon started walking across the land with Rosa tagging along. Mr. Witherspoon had cut off a green willow sapling that had a nice Y in it and held onto the two thin limbs with each hand. The small trunk of the willow was held straight out in front of him. They walked and walked, and Rosa could see that he was walking in some kind of a pattern, crisscrossing his path each time. Sometimes he would pause and then walk slowly on. After many hours, he stopped and said, "Wait, wait, I think we might jest have somethin' here. See, she's headin' down. Let's see, we'll try just thisaway. I'll turn a little, yes-siree, see, she's startin' to bounce, now watch close."

Rosa was fascinated with all this and watched the little willow bounce and then bend right down toward the ground. Mr. Witherspoon told her that, as a "water-witcher and a diviner," he had the gift to find water, and he was able to pass this power into the willow, and the willow would show him jest where the underground water was hidin'. After he made many more passes in the same area, crisscrossing in his pattern, he said, "Now there is some water here, but let's see if we can find some closer in to the cabin."

The three of them walked back and forth and did find some closer, up on the slight rise behind the cabin. "Wait, yes, this here's the spot," Mr. Witherspoon shouted, and he piled up some rocks in a small stack. "This here is where the water is; it's not too deep. Now if you don't run into a jumble of those lava rocks down there, it will be easy diggin', and then you will sure-nuf have good, sweet water. Yes-siree, this here's the spot; the water is sure-nuf down yonder."

Oh, Henry was so happy, he jumped up and down and grinned and asked, "Can I try, Mr. Witherspoon?" Well, Henry tried and tried, but the willow would not move for him one little bit. Of course Rosa wanted to try too, so she asked, "Mr. Witherspoon, do you suppose it might work for a girl?" So Rosa was handed the forked willow branch. She held it in both hands as he instructed. "Now hold tight, little sister; just make a fist under the stick; hold your hands upside down, see like this. Now take it easy, nice and slow, breathe deep and just mosey over thataway."

Henry and Mr. Witherspoon sat on their haunches in the shade of the old cottonwood while Rosa slowly walked over the side of the slope with the willow held tightly in outstretched fists. She felt very serious about this and just somehow knew that the willow would work for her. She was feeling disappointed after some time of walking back and forth but would not give up, no-siree, she was going to make it work. Then she thought she felt a tug with one hand, then a tug on the other. She stopped, and the branch out in front of her slowly dipped toward the ground. She could not stop it; she tightened up her hold, but the willow was like a living thing—it kept twisting in her fists, just kept twisting toward the earth no matter how hard she held to it. "Mr. Witherspoon, Henry," she called out, "come see; it's working, it's working; see, I can't hold it from turning. Does that mean there really is water down there somewhere?"

The men hurried over, and Mr. Witherspoon chuckled loudly, "Oh land-a-goshen, little sister, you are doin' it, you are water-witchin', you must have the divinin' spirit in you. Look at that thar willow, Henry; it sure is bobbin' down, and that's right near the spot I witched myself.

Here sister, move over this way to my final marker—now you're really goin' to feel somethin'."

Rosa stood where he had marked his spot. Then she felt the willow twisting almost completely around in her grip, and the end pointed right down to the ground. It was slightly bouncing a little; the force of the twisting willow was frightening to Rosa. "How can this be?" She called out, "Mr. Witherspoon, what kind of force is this? It's scary, I can't stop it from twisting, and I'm holding real tight. Is that God doing that?"

"Well, little sister," he answered and put his hand on her shoulder, "that must be God's doin' alright. He just gave a few of us the great divinin' spirit and also gave that old willow the know-how too; yep, you're right, it's God's doin's."

In the wonder of this unusual power, Rosa felt a little strange. She started shaking and felt like her legs would not hold her up, so she just sat down on the ground with the willow in her fists. Henry noticed her fright and knelt down and put his arm around her shoulder. "Well, Rosey, you have the divinin' gift to find water, and yep, I guess it might be a little bit scary."

"Mr. Witherspoon," Henry asked, "do all girls have this spirit to witch for water?" "Oh no, no-siree," he answered quickly, "I don't know of a one that can, but there was a woman over to Utah that I heerd of oncet, though, who could do the witchin'. Yes sir, this little sister is sure a humdinger; she sure is one good water-witcher. Jest too dern bad that she's a girl, else I would hire her myself to help me in my divinin' business."

That night and many nights, Rosa dreamed of the power she had felt in the small willow branch, of the wonder of something she could not understand. Maybe Miss Stanton could explain it. She would ask her. She went to sleep and dreamed of seeing the beautiful lady in the bright clouds. Oh, how she wanted to ask her about such a strange power!

Many times after this, Rosa pondered over what Mr. Witherspoon had said about her being a natural born "diviner," but too bad she was a girl. Well, she thought, why couldn't a girl be a diviner, same as a man? Why not? Then she always answered her own question—well, probably because there was no girl doing that kind of work, none at all, not anywhere in the country. Girls did not do those kinds of things. Well, girls didn't wear britches either, and girls didn't dig root cellars, and girls didn't trap rabbits, either. Girls didn't saw up sagebrush, and girls certainly did not ride their very own horse all alone all over the country-side. But if girls didn't do these things, then how come Rosa did? She was a girl; even if she wished she were a boy, she was still a girl. Well, she did these things because she wanted to, she liked to. She especially loved riding her Kit-horse anywhere she wanted. So why couldn't she be a water witcher too, a "diviner"? She would speak to brother Henry about this. Maybe he would help her to become a divinin' water-witcher, even if she was a girl.

The new well was painstakingly dug by Henry with the help of a neighboring farmer. Rosa was the go-fer for everything, and she helped spread out the dirt as it came up by the buckets full. Finally, when they did hit the water, it was very muddy for a long, long time, but when it did clear up, it was a good supply of nice, sweet water, just like Mr. Witherspoon, the water-witchin' diviner, had said it would be.

There was no money for a windmill as yet, so you just had to crank and crank on the rope with a bucket attached to bring up the water. Henry got a trough set up and some pipe, and soon there was enough water to keep some of the plants in the garden alive so that they would have a few cabbages and such for the winter. Of course, with Henry gone, it was Rosa's job to crank up the water bucket and fill the trough and bring in water for the household, and that took hours of hard, sweaty work.

Then that fall, a windmill was installed, and the next winter there was more rain in the area. They all hoped the drought was finally over and were all thankful that they had found water and could stay on and keep their homestead.

Since the wonderful gift of the Kit-horse from Uncle Albert, Rosa and brother Henry had been saving every cent they could. This was, of course, very difficult because most everything was bartered and traded in one way or another. But Henry wanted Rosa to have a real saddle, and he had told her, "By golly, Rosey, we will scrimp and save up enough to get you a saddle for that Kit-horse someday, and that there is a promise, little partner."

Well, that someday arrived about a year later. Henry brought home a small saddle for Rosa. She was almost as excited as when Kit had arrived. Henry told her, "Now, it's not a new one, Rosey; it's been used; it needs work done on it, but I got a new cinch and a saddle blanket. It'll look right smart after we do a heap of cleanin' on it. It's a small size and should be just right for you and Kit."

Right away they started on cleaning the leather with saddle soap and doing the repairs. Henry was very good at fixin' everything and knew just what to do. Within a few days the saddle leather was alive again. Rosa had spent hours soaping the saddle again and again with saddle soap and rubbing it and rubbing it with a clean sack. The leather just ate up the oil and soon started to look almost new. The blanket had brown and white stripes and was a heavy wool.

One early morning, the blanket and the polished saddle were carefully cinched onto Kit's back. That Kit let out several unpleasant snorts and danced around in protest. Rosa and Henry laughed at her and tried to calm her down. "Well," Henry chuckled, "it has been a long time since you had a saddle cinched on you, ol' Kit, but you're not foolin' us. You know very well what this is. Stop bein' so grouchy. Now, now, Kit, just settle down, you little Rebel horse."

Rosa was laughing hard; Kit looked so grumpy, hopping up and down and snorting like a spoiled brat. She had her back arched up in a big hump; she did not like this saddle thing one little bit. But they soon got her settled down, and she stood sullenly as Rosa slowly eased herself up into her very own saddle. Then, after a few more snorts and stiff-legged hops, Kit finally stopped protesting. Rosa tried to stop laughing and talked gently to her and patted her neck soothingly.

Oh, Rosa was in heaven now. She could carry heavier saddlebags behind her saddle, and when she rode into town or over to the neighbors now, she could pack home lots of things. She kept her Kit-horse brushed and clean at all times and her saddle oiled and shiny, too.

Sister Louisa would smile at her as she watched Rosa currying her horse. "Oh Rosey, honey, you spend so much time on that horse. You are getting to be a young lady now and should be takin' the cookin' and sewin' seriously. You know, we never finished that quilt we were working on for your hope-chest. Someday you'll have a husband and young ones to care for, then what will you do?"

Rosa always just agreed with sister Louisa about the wisdom of this but thought to herself, "Cook and sew and do washings? Oh no, I want to be out here with Kit, ridin' out over the prairie, listening to the call of the hawks. I would even rather tend my rabbit-trap than go work inside the cabin. I just don't have time to do those wearisome indoor chores."

Sister Louisa was only a few years older than Rosa, but about as different as day is from night. Louisa was a plumpish girl, with a pretty smile and soft wavy brown hair, and you could tell by looking at her that she had sweetness in her heart. She was very easy going and kind, a gentle lady. She loved to cook and loved to sew and look after folks. Oh, she would make some man a fine wife indeed.

Rosa was nearing her last year at Miss Stanton's school, and for some time now she had been proudly working for the town storekeeper. On Saturdays and Sunday afternoons she was caring for the store-keeper's four children. She enjoyed the little ones and took very good care of them at their home in town. Then she would saddle up Kit and ride like the wind back out to the Homestead in the evening. She was paid with food supplies and sometimes some cloth for Mama. After the last summer's work, she had been paid with a new pair of sturdy boots that laced up and had nice, square heels. The heels helped keep her foot securely in the stirrups at all times, no matter how fast Kit would run or turn. These were such happy years for Rosa. The Homestead was doing fine, and Mama was not having very many sick-spells, so Rosa could be outside most of the time.

The wagon and the work-horses were wonderful additions to the Homestead, especially for Mama; now she could go to church every Sunday. Rosa had learned how to throw the complicated harness up onto the sturdy backs of the horses and hitch Barney and Maybelle up to the farm wagon. It was pretty difficult for her to throw the heavy harness way up on the rumps of the horses, but somehow she managed it by stepping up on a wooden box.

Now on Sundays, the three ladies would put on their bonnets and throw on their best shawls, and Rosa would trot those big horses right down the road. The ladies were so happy they would laugh and sing the whole way into town. Rosa's Mama had the most beautiful singing voice. It was clear and pure, and when she sang her favorite hymns or some of those old Irish songs, Rosa thought it was the most wonderful sound in all the world. Louisa sang well too, but Rosa could never seem to let out much more than a hoarse murmur. "I still can't carry a tune in a basket," she would say, and they would all laugh.

Sometimes Louisa would be needed to work in town too, at the hotel. Rosa would drive her into town in the wagon. Louisa was gaining a reputation for being one special cook. Her pies were luscious and sweet and in great demand, especially her gooseberry pies. Rosa was quick to realize that by picking the wild gooseberries when they were in season, she could make extra change by selling them to the hotel.

Louisa cooked up the tart gooseberries with lots and lots of sugar. They were a special treat cooked up into a pie or made up into a jam. Picking the wild gooseberries was very hard work because the small bushes were covered with big thorns. Rosa had to wear gloves and a heavy jacket, but she knew how wonderful that gooseberry jam would taste next winter when it was brought up from Rosa's root cellar in its special canning jar. It was a way of making those few extra pennies, too.

Rosa and her little buckskin became well known to the other homesteaders, the townspeople of Springfield, and the folks in the other little settlement of Pingree. Rosa loved these kindhearted folks and would stop and chat when she could, or just wave and smile. She often thought about the difference in these folks and the hateful ways of the people in Indiana who always labeled her and her family "Those Rebels."

Rosa, wearing her rabbit-skin coat and riding her single-footing buckskin at a fast clip, must have been an unusual sight. She was still very small and wiry and always wore her brown hair done up in a long braid hanging down her back. The slouch hat she wore was somewhat of a cross between a stetson and a border hat, but very well worn. If not for the braid and the long woolen skirt, she easily would have passed for a boy.

Not all the folks were friendly, however. Rosa did have to look out for a few of the older boys of the town; even a couple of boys in her school loved to taunt Rosa. They called her "Bucktooth Scotty" and other unpleasant things. Evidently they did not like to see a "girl" being so independent and riding her own horse. Sometimes the jeering of the boys was very upsetting to Rosa, but she just held her head up high and pranced little Kit right by her tormenters as if she were a regal lady. No, she would not get into any more fights. She was almost grown up now, and besides she did not want to upset her mama.

In the fall of 1910 when Rosa turned fifteen, she was now in her last year of schooling at Miss Stanton's one room schoolhouse in Springfield. She had caught up with her grade level many years before and loved her schooling very much.

She often stayed after school when she could, to help Miss Stanton correct papers and such. Many times when Rosa said good-by to Miss

Stanton and walked out to the corral, she thought of how much she would miss the friendship of her teacher when she graduated. Oh, she would be able to see her, but it just would not be the same. Rosa admired Miss Stanton so much; she was a very dedicated teacher. Rosa knew that she and all the other students were lucky indeed to have such a sincere teacher. Miss Stanton had dedicated her whole life to this school and all the students attending here. Oh yes, she was still that same unsmiling, stern lady, but Rosa knew that underneath was a true teacher, one whose future was dedicated to her students. And Miss Stanton's own thirst for more and more knowledge was a wonderment to Rosa.

Miss Stanton wanted her students to learn and to understand what was in their schoolbooks, but she also was quick to tell them what was happening in their small community, in their county, their state, and in their land of America. She helped them discuss any current event in the newspaper. She received a paper from her home town of Salt Lake City and one from a friend in Chicago, Illinois. In this way the children learned about the invention of the electric light way back East and about the truly strange invention of a thing called a "telephone." You could just talk through a wire to another person far, far away. The concepts of the electric light and the telephone were very difficult for the children to understand, and they asked many questions.

Then one day, Miss Stanton brought a most amazing thing to school to show them. It was a talking machine, a "graphophone." It was a nicely finished box-like thing with a big flower-horn sticking up. It used round records that she said were made of wax. When Miss Stanton wound up the box, a thing went around and around and out came singing and musical instruments playing wondrous sounds. Standing around the table, each child was spellbound listening to this incredible machine. Some of the songs were "Columbia, Gem of the Ocean" and "Darling Nellie Gray." Oh, this was indeed a miracle to behold.

Miss Stanton was also a gifted storyteller. She read stories and poetry from her books, but she often told stories of other people and other lands just as if she knew them personally. One story that Rosa had heard many times was the story of how Miss Stanton actually met the President, Theodore "Teddy" Roosevelt, face to face. She had made a special trip up into Colorado when he was to make a train stop there. She walked right up to him at the train depot and introduced herself. She told him she was a schoolteacher from Springfield, Idaho, that she had twenty-two students in all grades, and that they were all admirers of the President. Well, he shook her hand and smiled at her with those big, white teeth and said, "Miss Stanton, what a grand privilege to meet you. You know, I wish I could stand in your schoolroom and give a rousing speech to your students and then shake each one of them by the hand. Will you give them a message from me? Tell them that knowledge is the key to life and the gateway to happiness. And just bully for you, Miss Stanton, for coming all this way to meet me. You schoolmarms are the backbone of this great land, this United States of America. God bless you, my dear."

CHAPTER SEVEN

The Cowhand

ONE LATE FALL EVENING, as Rosa was leaving the one room schoolhouse, she was again thinking about her teacher. She quickly slipped the hackamore on the willing Kit and threw her blanket on the sleek back. Then the saddle, getting it cinched up in one quick motion. She swung up into the saddle easily. Kit was ready at once with one light touch of Rosa's heel, and she hit her single-footing amble just as soon as Rosa headed her out onto the packed roadway. Kit knew she was headed home to her ration of oats and her snug barn for the night.

It was snowing only lightly, but it was very cold. This feels like a serious storm blowing up, Rosa thought. She huddled up into her warm skin coat and tucked her woolen skirt tightly around the rabbit skin leggings. Her slouch hat was pulled tightly down on her head with a leather thong under her chin. Rosa did not mind the cold; she was used to being out in all kinds of weather, and she was looking forward to a swift run home. Her thoughts again turned to her teacher and how, just today, Miss Stanton had asked Rosa if she would like to come into the school as a helper-teacher. Of course there would be no pay, but it would be very nice to be a real helper-teacher. Rosa always enjoyed teaching the younger children, and if she was there, she would still be able to learn more things from Miss Stanton, just as she had been doing. Yes, she would ask her mama and Louisa about this and also talk it over with her partner, Henry.

My goodness, it's snowing harder now, and there is that cold wind blowing the snow straight across the land. But there was still some daylight left and only three miles to home and one of Louisa's hearty rabbit stews. Rosa just closed her eyes against the wind as she often did, with no concern at all that her Kit-horse could follow the road safely home in any kind of weather.

They were about halfway to home; the graceful Kit was ambling along in her fastest rolling gait; then, just where the road took a dip across a gully surrounded by willow trees, Kit stumbled. She let out a loud grunt and went down fast. Rosa flew straight off the saddle before she could pull up on the reins. She tumbled to the ground hard and kept rolling in front of the horse.

Rosa was stunned from the fall, and she lay crumpled up on the packed roadway. She tried to shake her head to clear the haze in her eyes. She thought she heard voices, and yes, she looked up from the road and there were two boys, and one of them was standing directly over her. He was jumping up and down shouting with glee. "We got her; see, wha' did I tell ya, she wears britches." As Rosa tried to find her way out of the haze, she actually felt him reach down and lift up her skirt. "Them thar's squaw britches, see, I told ya so, she really is an injun. Well, Miss hoity-toity squaw, we gotcha now, and we're gonna teach you a thing or two, yes siree, we're gonna teach you somethin'."

Now there were three boys dancing around her as she lay stunned on the ground. But then something exploded inside Rosa. She looked back at Kit. Kit was down, her little horse was struggling to pull her legs under her to stand up. "Oh, oh, oh, oh no," she moaned aloud. "What have you done, you tripped my Kit, you broke her leg, she can't get up. Oh no, you've killed my Kit!" And she came off the ground like a wild animal, screaming and scratching at the boy above her, "You've broken her leg, I'll kill you, I'll kill you all!"

She had the fury of a demon as she knocked the boy down and rolled over and over with him, pummeling him with all her wiry strength. There was something else going on around her, but Rosa only felt the red fury and pure hatred in her heart and the desire to kill this stupid boy who had hurt her beloved Kit.

Suddenly, she felt a very strong arm circle her waist and lift her off the struggling boy. She hung there off the ground, arms and legs flailing about, spitting mad and still screaming. Then she saw another long arm reach out and backhand the boy as he was getting up. The boy was knocked back down again, and he hit the roadway very hard.

"Da girrl, you hurt," a deep voiced boomed, "da lid-dle horse, you hurt, pick on da Kleinesmadchen, get avay or you get hurt, you dummkopfs," and the voice kept getting louder, "you hurt da Kleinesmadchen again, I fint you, I hurt you, you hear me? I hurt you."

The man was speaking in very broken English, but his anger and his threats were very understandable. Rosa could see all three boys scattering like quail into the brush.

Then, just as soon as Rosa felt her feet touch the ground, she ran back to Kit. "Oh Kit, oh my little horse," and the tears were streaming down her face. The little buckskin had staggered to her feet, but she was wobbly and holding one small foreleg gingerly off the ground.

Very quickly the big man was there, patting Kit's neck and gently running his hand down along the leg to the fetlock. "Nein, nein," he said quietly, "not broke, goot, not broke, she da tough mustang, ya?"

Rosa looked up at him through blurred eyes. He was a large, square man in heavy cowboy gear, the slouched wide-brimmed hat covering his head was dripping rain and snow, and a black curly beard covered his face. "Not broken, you say, not broken, are you sure?" Rosa cried out. "You say not broken. Oh Kit, it's not broken! They must have tripped her, those cruel boys." And she started sobbing openly as she felt the anger mounting inside her again. She had never, ever felt such hatred for anyone.

"Now, now, Kleinesmadchen," the cowboy said soothingly, "mustang be ok, leg not broke, but could be you hurt? You fall hard, und you roll fast, dat smart ting, to roll."

"No, no, I'm not hurt," Rosa said hurriedly, "But Kit, her leg is hurt; are you sure it's not broken? I know a horse has to be put down if it's leg gets broken."

"No, not broke, I know da horse, da remuda boss I am, care da many horse, doctor da many horse, no Liebchen, not broke."

Rosa was gulping air to keep from falling over. Yes, the cowboy would certainly know what to do for Kit—as long as the leg was not broken, she might be alright. Rosa tried to stand very still and steady herself, holding Kit's reins as the man again leaned over, massaging Kit's foreleg. Kit also stood very still, her big brown eyes holding Rosa's blue ones in quiet understanding.

"Not da leg," he was saying almost to himself. "It da knee joint. See across road is da rope stretched; she hit da rope mit knee, not leg; vould have broke da leg for sure. Knee hurt, but be OK in time, need da rubbing."

"Miss, you can valk da roan over? In bags get linment." Rosa quickly looked in the direction of his waving hand, and back in the gully was a large roan saddlehorse nipping at scrub brush as unconcerned as anything.

Rosa managed to make her legs work and gently approached the horse and talked quietly to him. He threw up his head and snorted, backing away, but soon she was able to gently pick up his trailing reins and lead him over to the man and Kit. This was a very large horse, she noticed, and the saddle and gear were all those of a working cowhand. She had seen many such horses and their cowboy riders in town, as there were several huge cattle ranches in this part of Idaho.

The cowboy dug quickly into his saddlebag and came up with a small, flat, brown bottle. "Linment," he said, hesitated a moment, and then said almost to himself, "Nein, nein, linment not goot yet; ve need da cold on dat bruise; ve use da snow, pack da snow on da knee." He scooped up handfuls of the powdery snow and held it against Kit's leg. Then he looked up at Rosa again, "Miss, see in da bag, fint shirt, ve cut, ve use for bind snow on da knee."

Rosa was quick to reply, "Oh no, no, mister, not your shirt, not yours. Here, I can use my skirt. It's wool. Do you have a knife? I'll make a binding for Kit."

The cowboy looked down at her as she quickly dropped her skirt and knelt down, smoothing the skirt out on the snow, ready to cut it up. He could not help but grin a little. Here was the little munchkin, kneeling there in her leather britches and rabbit fur coat. The long brown hair had escaped its braid, and the wet hair was flying all over her face and shoulders. "OK, liebchen, OK, here da knife, but hat, vere da hat? Not good da vet head; vait, I find da hat."

Rosa looked up at him from the ground when he handed her the hat, and he seemed like a giant, a great black-bearded avenging giant of an angel. He had saved her Kit, and he had saved her from heaven knows what with those awful boys. Her head was spinning around and around, and she tried to steady herself with both hands on the ground.

She looked up at him again as he stood above her, and there, circling around his dripping hat, was a soft glow, and yes, there was the beautiful lady's face, smiling down at Rosa. It was only a fleeting thing, but she knew it was the guardian angel Mama had told her was always near Rosa, looking over her.

Then she looked again at the slight grin on his face and the startling white teeth in the dark beard. She drew a big sigh and tried to smile back at him. Well, yes, it must be kind of funny to see a girl just drop her skirt, just like that.

It was almost dark now. The cowboy had expertly wrapped Kit's leg with part of the skirt and tied it securely with leather thongs from his saddle. "Now, ve go," he said. "How far, da homeplace?"

"'Bout a mile and a half," Rosa told him. And he quickly said, "Goot, da roan you ride, vait Miss," and he took his slicker from behind his saddle and helped her put her head through the hole and get her hat back on. "You varmer now; you need to varm; home soon; mustang be OK. I stop und put da fresh snow on da leg. You stay on roan, OK now?" he smiled at her as he handed her the reins. "Roan testy, you valk him behint da mustang, he be OK."

This was to be the longest ride of Rosa's life, she was so concerned about her Kit. Kit had to be alright, she had to be, and this cowboy who took care of lots of horses, a whole remuda of horses, should know. Then she was dizzy and would have to concentrate real hard just to hold herself in the saddle. She gripped the large round saddlehorn with both hands, holding the reins loosely. Her head was spinning, and she felt sick all over. She was cold and shivering even inside the heavy tent-like slicker. A terrible throbbing started in her head, and one of her legs felt awful painful, but the pain probably kept her from actually passing out.

The cowboy stopped a couple of times and lifted Kit's leg. He unwound the wrap and massaged the knee and leg, then wrapped it again with more snow and walked slowly through the blowing snow, leading the little horse, with the roan following, and Rosa holding on tight to the big round saddle-horn.

Two beams of light from kerosene lamps streamed out the windows of the cabin and another from the open barn door. Rosa knew Mama and Louisa would be very worried. She had never been this late coming home from school, and with the storm and all. As they slowly walked into the light streaming across the yard, Mama came rushing out the door calling, "Rosa, is that you? Rosa, are you hurt? Rosey, what has happened?"

"No, Mama," Rosa managed to cry out, "No, Mama, I'm alright, but Kit is hurt. It's her leg, her knee joint. She's hurt, Mama. This cowboy helped us; he knows about horses, Mama," and her voice trailed off into tears.

The cowboy reached up and gently picked Rosa off the roan. "Ma'am, di Kleinesmadchen OK, in da shock I tink, she be OK ma'am." And he quickly carried Rosa into the cabin behind Mama and gently lay her on the bed where Louisa was throwing back quilts. Mama hurriedly took off the large slicker and covered Rosa, smoothing back the wet hair from her face and checking to make sure she had no broken bones. Louisa hastened over to the stove for hot water and a wash pan and clean cloths.

Da mustang I see to, Ma'am," the cowboy said, hat in hand standing just inside the door. "Oh, thank you, sir, thank you," Mama said as she looked over at him. "There is feed in the barn. Oh, I do hope Kit will be alright. That Kit is Rosa's whole life, and I thank you, sir; I thank the Lord for your help. I'll be out soon as we get Rosa settled."

Out in the small lean-to barn, he again removed the wrap from Kit, felt the bones and tendons carefully, then put fresh snow on his wrap and tied it back on her knee. The little horse was not steady on her legs, and he was concerned she might lie down, which he knew would not be good. He found a brush and curry comb and curried and brushed the little horse until she was warmer and stood steadier. He managed to get her to take some water, and then he began to coax her to eat some oats from his hand.

Mama quietly entered the barn and was watching the burly looking cowboy talking gently to the mustang. He is German, Mama knew; her own papa had been German. This fellow can barely speak English. What is a German doing out here in the West? Most German settlements were in the midwest, but he is a real cowhand, no doubt about that. Well, she thought, he can be anything, he can be anything at all; he helped my Rosa.

Of course Rosa had told Mama about the boys tripping up her Kit and how fighting mad she was and how this cowboy had suddenly been there and scared off the boys and took care of Kit. Yes, Mama thought, this cowboy has my gratitude, my undying gratitude, and she shuddered to think what might have happened to her Rosa if this cowboy had not come along at just the right time. Then she thought for a long moment to recall any of her German. It had been so many years since she had spoken German with her father, but they had spoken the language almost continually when she was growing up.

"We are in your debt, sir," Mama said quietly in halting German. "Our gratitude cannot be put into words. Rosa Ellen is a very precious girl, and we thank you, sir."

He looked up, startled, and stepped back into the shadows beside the horses. Then he replied in his own fluid German, "That is alright, Ma'am; those were cruel boys, but they will not bother your girl again. How is the little one? I think she might have injured her leg, as she was favoring it, and she was probably suffering from shock, too. 'Alright' you say? That is good. I am surprised, Ma'am, that you speak the German, not many people do out here."

Mama moved up to pat Kit and told him, "Oh, my own papa was German. We lived in Indiana. Papa taught me to speak when I was a child. It's been a very long time ago, but I understand most of your words. What is your name?"

"They call me E.J., Ma'am; I work out at the Circle W for Mr. Wiley."

"Well, Mr. E.J.," Mama told him, "you'll not be going any further tonight in this storm. You just put up your horse here in the barn. I see you have a bedroll there, and there is plenty of clean straw up in the loft for you to stay the night. Will Kit really be alright?"

He explained to her in German that the knee joint had hit the taut rope first, and that that was a good thing, because if she had hit her shin bone, her leg would have broken. But she would be fine with cold packs for now and then linament rubs later.

"Oh," Mama sighed, "that is so good to hear. Now, soon as you get the horses bedded down, you come directly to the cabin. We'll have a hot supper ready for you." Then she quickly rushed out of the barn before he could answer.

Hurrying across the yard, Mama already knew that this was no ordinary cowboy. He spoke as a highly educated German, and he was not happy giving his name. But no matter, the West had always been a place where folks did not ask questions, and even in this year of 1910, folks still didn't ask too many questions of strangers. This unlikely cowhand is an angel in disguise, so he is not a stranger and will never be a stranger to this Scott family.

A short time later he knocked and stepped inside the cabin with hat in hand. Mama said, "Oh good, your supper is hot; you can wash up just there by the door. Here, I'll hang your coat," and she took his things from him. Soon he was sitting at the table, his heavy black hair slicked back as best he could. Mama thought, "That hair is so wavy that nothing could tame it down. He must be one of those black southern Germans; they have very dark hair, the very opposite of most Germans, who are fair and blond."

She served him a plateful of steaming stew and introduced him to Louisa. They watched him eat with gusto, and she realized he was much younger than she had thought: Why, he's hardly more than a boy, but certainly a big sturdy fellow, tall and thick chested. He looks at ease in that cowboy garb, very confident. Well, some people from Europe have that "ease" about them, but not many that I've seen, and he certainly is not from peasant stock.

He asked again about Rosa, and Mama told him in her halting German, "Well, little Rosey has some bruises, and that leg will be mighty sore too, and I think she hit her head pretty hard. She has a big goose egg on her temple, but she'll be alright. Louisa brewed up some of her special herb tea and saw to it that Rosa drank the whole mug. So right now and for all the night long, she will be out like a light, and that's best for her. She wanted to run out to see if Kit was alright, but I told her what you said, and that Kit was in good hands, so she settled down."

As Louisa served him another helping of the stew, Mama asked, "Please tell me, Mr. E.J., did those boys hurt our Rosa?" She looked directly into his eyes; they were a startling hazel green. Mama was almost shocked at the brilliant color.

"No, Frau Scott, no Ma'am. I was some distance when the mustang went down, but I saw it all. The roan is fast; we reached there just as the little one came up fighting. She was like a wild-cat, tearing into that big boy with great fury. No, Ma'am, other than the fall, she was not touched." Mama breathed a sigh of relief and held her head in her hands for a moment.

The cowboy rose and told them in his broken English, "Tanks for da fine stew, da rabbit vas it not? So tasty." Then he turned to Mama and spoke in German, "I'll be leaving at first light, Frau Scott, but will swing by tomorrow at dusk on my way back out to the ranch. I'll check on the mustang again if that is alright. That snow pack should help the knee considerably. I will keep fresh snow on the knee during the night, but it should also be cold packed often tomorrow, and some light exercise would be good for her a couple of times tomorrow, too. Just walk her around the yard a couple of times so the leg does not stiffen up. And Frau Scott, if you have vinegar, a half cup over her grain once a day would be good for her. Goodnight ladies, thank you again for a most delicious meal." And he went quietly out the door.

Mama and Louisa looked at each other and both just held up their hands in wonder as if to say, "Lands-a-goshen, that is one unusual young man that saved our Rosey." Mama translated all that he had said to Louisa as best she could, and Louisa said, "Well, Mama, he is certainly no ordinary cowboy. For one thing, he is German. Isn't that strange? And also the cowhands we see in town are dirty and rough talking and scrawny lookin', and they all walk around with a big chew of tobaccy in one cheek. This one is very different for sure, and he seems like a real gentleman."

"Yes," Mama agreed, "a gentleman, well educated, and he knows about doctorin' horses, that's for sure, and the Good Lord put this one man right where he was needed today. My prayers will be for him and the guardian angel that was looking over our Rosey tonight."

By daybreak the cowboy E.J. was gone, and Mama and Louisa had a tough time keeping Rosa down. Finally they let her get up and go out into the barn to see for herself that Kit was doing alright. Louisa had packed the binding with snow several times and walked Kit around a bit.

At dusk Rosa was in the barn and heard his horse coming into the yard. She limped quickly to the barn door. He stepped down and dropped the roan's reins by the water trough, then came over and tipped his hat. "Vel, Miss, how da mustang do?"

Rosa hurried him inside saying, "Oh, she is better, I think. See, she can put more of her weight on that leg, but she still limps badly when I lead her. We have done all the things you told Mama should be done— do you think she is better?"

He patted Kit, ran his hand down her withers, and picked up the hoof, feeling very carefully around the leg and knee. "Ya, ya, no svelling, she bedder. She be OK; in few veeks, goot as new. Here is linment, rub leg, but use da snow pack noder two day, den rub linment easy all round joint and leg. Leave off da binding when use da linment. She need da valking offen, und da double feed, use da vinegar in da oats. Ya, ya, she be fine, mustang tough; she tough liddle mustang."

Rosa was so nervous, she wanted to tell the cowboy how very grateful she was, but couldn't seem to find her tongue. She finally blurted out, "Mr. E.J., I . . . I . . . we are eternally in your debt; you saved my Kit. I . . . we . . . well, we are all so grateful to you." Her planned speech came out in short bursts, and he smiled at her, an understanding smile.

"Dat OK, Miss, to be dere, I vas happy, mustang mean much. You keep da liddle one in goot condition, I can tell. Vel, I go now."

"Oh no, no," Rosa cried out. "Mama said you are to come in to supper; you'll have to, she has set a place for you."

At supper, Mama tried not to pry, but she had to ask E.J. where he was from. His reply was in German. "Stuttgart, Germany, Frau Scott. Where was your papa from?" And she found that she was the one answering questions for most of the meal.

Louisa and Rosa were naturally quiet during this conversation, trying to be at ease. But this was not an everyday occurrence in their lives, having a strange man at their table, and even more unusual, a German cowboy.

As they finished, he rose and said, "Again, I tank you ladies veddy much, supper vonderful. Our cookie only goot mit da beans und biscuits and notting else," and he grinned. "Go now, I must." Then he looked at Rosa, "Now, Miss, you care for mustang goot. She be fine; no ride few veeks, den only da short vays. Von month she be fine, go like da vind. Gutnacht to you ladies," and he was quickly gone. They were all three very quiet as they listened to the rapid hoofbeats drifting away into the night.

The next month was wearing on Rosa. She had recovered from her fall alright, but now she had to walk to and from school. She still had her chores, her lessons, and had to take care of Kit, too. No one at school said anything except to ask why she was not riding her horse. Rosa wanted to shout at everyone, "Those cruel boys tried to cripple my Kit," but she said nothing about the incident to anyone; she only said, "Kit stepped in a gopher hole and needs a rest-time for a while."

The two boys from school and the bully from town never came anywhere near her. They made a wide berth around wherever Rosa was, and the school boys sat unnecessarily quiet at their desks all through the school day. And right after school, they disappeared quickly.

After the month, Kit was doing so well that Rosa knew she could ride her to school. She just walked her, but Kit was eager to go faster. After another week, Rosa let her tack out a few times during the ride home.

One day, as she was leaving the school yard, she saw a rider coming along the road. She knew it was Mr. E.J. on his roan, and she knew that the boys who had attacked her had also seen him. She wondered if this was just a happenstance. No, the cowboy had undoubtedly planned it that way. She smiled and waved her hat at him.

E.J. reined in the roan and stood waiting for her. He was grinning back at her. "I greet you, Miss Scott. Da Kit mustang fine I see; fit she looks—goot for you."

"Hello, Mr. E.J.," Rosa said and could not help laughing out loud. "Mr. E.J., did you ride by here at just this time on purpose? Look at those boys go; they are really scared! Oh, that is so funny." And she laughed again.

"Vel, maybe dat is so," and he laughed too. "I ride your vay, alright?" Rosa nodded, and suddenly she felt a little light-headed, so she let Kit out into her singlefooting pace, maybe to show off just a little, and called to him, "And you'll stay to supper, too. Mama would not hear of you not staying for supper."

Rosa heard a chuckle as he drew up closer to her, "Vel, only if she serve dat invigeratin' rabbit stew." After awhile they rode side by side, and Rosa asked him, "How come you know so much about doctorin' horses?"

He looked over at her with those startling hazel green eyes and said seriously, "My papa had da many draft horse dat pull da brewery vagons. I care for da horse all my life. Vat grade in school you are, Miss?"

When Rosa told him she was going to graduate the eighth grade next spring, he seemed surprised. "Kleinesmadchen veddy goot mit da learnin', I tink."

Indeed, Mama would not hear of him going on without supper, so he stayed. He and Mama visited during the meal, but it was mostly about Idaho and the crops and about the huge cattle ranch of Mr. Wiley's near Springfield.

As he was leaving, standing by the door, hat in hand, he asked in German, "Frau Scott, would it be alright if I stopped by again around

Christmas? After that we will be moving the herds, and, and, we will be gone for some months." Then he added a little embarrassedly, "And I really should check on the mustang one more time to see if any splints are occurring in that leg."

Mama smiled at him and said cheerfully, "Oh yes, yes, please come for Christmas day, Mr. E.J. Can you come for Christmas? Our brother Henry will be home, and we will have a fine celebration. Now we will expect you, so don't disappoint us."

This time when he went out the door, Rosa and Louisa stood out on the front porch and waved good-by to him. He raised his hat and smiled at them and rode away into the dusk. Louisa patted Rosa's shoulder and hurried back into the cabin. Rosa just stood there, looking up the road where he disappeared. Oh my, she thought, oh my, Mr. E.J., you are not like anyone I have ever seen before, but I know who you are. You are my avenging angel. You are the avenging angel that was sent down to help my Kit when we needed you. I know that's who you are.

Well, there was plenty to talk about for the next month, and plenty to do. It was easier for Rosa, since she was able to ride Kit to school and stay a few hours if she was needed by Miss Stanton after school. She was still working on Saturdays and part of Sundays taking care of the storekeeper's children. With her chores and all, it was a very busy time.

They were all looking forward to Christmas. Henry would be home, and now they would be having a very special guest for Christmas supper. Oh, it was so exciting, they made great plans. Rosa knew where there was a kind of tree. She would cut it herself and drag it home behind Kit. It was not really a pine tree; it was really just a scraggly bush, but it would do fine. It would be real pretty with berries and popcorn strands. Mama had some red wool that she cut into strips, and that made pretty braids and bows also to go around it.

Mama started singing Christmas carols right after Thanksgiving, and Rosa and Louisa always joined in her songs. Then they would get their usual laugh out of Rosa's efforts to find the right tune, but Rosa laughed too; she was used to the teasing.

Henry came home the week before Christmas and brought a big load of hay and other staples they needed. They were very busy, and Henry and Rosa made a survey of what she had been doing outside. They worked several days on some repairs to the barn and put up a new chicken house. Some varmint, probably a wolverine, had been killing chickens, and they needed to make the pen more secure. There were so many animals wanting to get to a fat hen, especially in the winter. The old red rooster, who hated Rosa, was still harassing her every chance he got, but Rosa laughed at him now. "You're gettin' too old to peck at my heels ol' Red, way too old. I can outrun you now."

There was no sleep for Rosa on Christmas Eve. She was really keyed up with anticipation for tomorrow. Sure, Henry was home and it was Christmas, and well, they were going to have a guest for Christmas. Anyway she really loved Christmas, so maybe that's why she was so excited and anxious for tomorrow to get here.

Very early Christmas morning she was in the barn finishing her chores when she heard the roan's hoofbeats trotting into the yard. She ran to the door and stood there as he stepped down. He was just as big and solid and square as she remembered. It was a cold windy day, and she watched as he threw off the black slicker, quickly rolled it up and tied it off on the back of his saddle. Suddenly her stomach was tied in a knot, and she felt sickly. What is this?

He turned and smiled at her standing there, and her heart went flip-flop ka-plunk, and she held tight to the barn door. "Meddy Christmas, Miss Scott," he called, "Da Kit horse is ok?"

She found her tongue. "Merry Christmas to you, Mr. E.J.; oh, Kit is fine. Come see her; she is just as good as new."

He patted the mare and was leaning over to run his hand down her leg. He had taken off his hat, and Rosa could see the dark, curling hair along his neck. She almost reached out and touched the back of his head. She wanted to run her hand through those curls but jerked her hand back, realizing that this would not be a proper thing to do.

"Val, she OK, no splints, goot job, Miss Ros-ah, goot job." He stood and looked down at her and smiled, those white even teeth making a startling contrast in the dark beard. The hazel eyes were laughing when he asked, "Now, haf you had troubles from dose boys at all?"

Rosa smiled back, "No sir, none at all. They clear out of my way when they see me coming, and I thank you again."

"Velcome you are, I'm sure. How is da mama and Miss Louisa?"

"Oh, come on in, Mr. E.J. They are fine, and I want you to meet my brother Henry. Henry and I are partners on this Homestead, you see. He is my big brother, and we are so happy to have him home for Christmas this year." She was just chattering along as they slowly walked across the yard.

The Christmas supper was extra nice with two big roasted chickens, savory dressing, and cornbread with plum sauce. There were roasted carrots, potatoes, turnips, and some wild roots that Rosa had dug up for Louisa.

Sister Louisa knew all about the wild roots and herbs. In later life Rosa would often say, "Oh, why didn't I learn those things from Louisa; she knew about all the wild things. She knew which roots and wild plants to flavor things and which ones would cure many aches. She always brewed up a fine tea that helped almost anything that ailed a person. I don't even know how she knew all those things. How silly of me not to have asked her and learned about those wonderful wild herbs and roots from my dear sister Louisa."

There was jovial talk around the table that Christmas day of 1910, and they all sat for hours savoring Louisa's pumpkin pies and hot herb tea. Mr. E.J. actually became very talkative. He talked of his childhood in Germany after Henry asked him about his family. He had trouble with his words, so he asked Mama to interpret.

He told them he had nine brothers and two sisters and that they were all older than he. His father was a fine brewmaster in Stuttgart; the family had three breweries and many wagons and large dray horses. My task, since I was young was to help with the horses. We had large underground stables under the breweries. I learned how to keep the horses healthy and fit. I also helped keep the harnesses clean and all the brass and silver polished at all times. It was a wonderful sight to see a six-horse-hitch in all their finery, pulling the huge red wagon filled with large casks of beer. Each horse had his own personal set of sleigh bells, and you better put the right set of bells on the right horse or else there was trouble. Those horses knew which set of bells was their very own.

Other than speaking of his younger years, Mr. E.J. did not venture more about himself. Then Henry asked him in a serious voice, "Mr. E.J., I have been reading and hearing about the threat of war in Europe and all the goin's on of the Emperor of Germany, that Kaiser Wilhelm. Is he going to make trouble? What do you think will happen?"

E.J. was quiet for a moment, then spoke to Mama in German. Rosa could feel the sorrow in his voice, even in this strange language. Mama told them what he was saying. "He says, yes, there is war coming; it has been coming for many years. The Emperor is leading the German people into a war to conquer the world, so he tells them. Germans are a strong, determined people, and now they will follow the Emperor's teaching as though he were a god. It is so very sad to see what is happening to my people. I do not agree with the Kaiser's teachings, but all my brothers and my father believe in him. They will fight if he says they must. I think all Germany will suffer, as war, with its death and sacrifice for all peoples, is never the answer. But when power hungry men lead a country, there is no other way. Some Germans know this and are trying to stop this crazy charge to war, but they won't be able to stop it. I feel all Europe will suffer, and I think this United States of America is wise to say they will not get involved. But who knows; it seems to me that the whole world will be caught up in this someday, if Kaiser Wilhelm has his way."

There were so many questions that Rosa wanted to ask him, and she knew there were many that Henry would like to ask too, but then Mama stood up and said, "This is a blessed day, and now we will have some Christmas caroling."

She stood in the center of the small cabin, with the rich smells of the supper and the satisfying scent of cinnamon and cloves simmering in the apple cider that Louisa was brewing on the big iron stove. Louisa's cider was a special treat for Christmas.

Mama folded her hands and started singing in her clear, sweet voice. It was a lovely Christmas carol from her childhood and one that Rosa had loved all her life. They were silent, listening to the pure, bell-like clarity of her voice. When she finished, she laughed and said, "Now, let's all sing 'Come All Ye Faithful.'"

She started, and one by one they all stood beside her and sang along. Mr. E.J. stood back and listened a while, but Mama reached out her hand to him, and he stepped closer and joined in. He just hummed along, but his rich baritone was like silk and very distinguishable from the family's voices. Henry had a quavering tenor voice, and Mama and Louisa were clear, sweet sopranos. Rosa was almost ashamed to add her odd tones, but joined in with gusto when Mr. E.J. smiled at her in understanding.

After the first song, they really got into the spirit, and "Jingle Bells" was a rousing medley. They were all quiet for a moment, and then Mr. E.J. stood a little taller and started to sing in his own language, "Stille

Nacht, Heilige Nacht" ("Silent Night, Holy Night"), and his voice was strong and clear. They could tell that he had sung this many times before. Everyone was silent, listening to the hauntingly sad tone in his husky voice.

"Oh," Rosa thought, "he is a homesick boy, a little boy homesick for his own family and for his own country." Tears came in her eyes, and when he looked at her, he knew she understood his pain.

The next morning after a fine breakfast, Mr. E.J. stood by his chair and tried to thank everyone for a wonderful Christmas. When he was thanking Louisa for such delicious food, he smiled broadly at her. As Rosa watched Louisa and Mr. E.J. smiling at each other, she thought, "Of course, Louisa is such a pretty girl, of course Mr. E.J. would like her; maybe that's why he came back to visit us." She suddenly felt a pang of something like pain start in her chest. Well, well, if that's the way it was, then she would be happy for Louisa—dear, sweet Louisa would make any man so very proud to have her.

Rosa went out with Mr. E.J., as she had to feed the stock. It was a cold day, but bright and clear. They did not talk while he saddled up the roan, and as he was leading him out into the yard, he turned and said to her, "Miss Scott, you und your family, I tank veddy much. You are goot, kind people, and proud I am to know you. Und Miss Scott, ah, you look so grown-up last night in da blue gown, da blue of dose eyes." He looked in her eyes, and Rosa suddenly felt very, very strange. She felt a flush in her neck and face. Why, no one had ever told her anything like that before. She stuttered, "Well, well, why Mr. E.J., I, I thank you, but you see, I am all grown-up; I was fifteen years old in October."

He took one step back and bumped into the roan, "Vel, vel, I, I, did not know dat, Miss Rose-ah, I tot, I tot. . . ." Rosa interrupted him with a laugh, "Oh yes, Mr. E.J., I know, I know you thought that I was very young, I could tell. And Mama told me that 'kleinesmadchen' means a little child."

He smiled broadly and tipped his hat to her, "Vell goot-by, Miss Rose-ah, Miss grown-up Rose-ah Ellen Scott, und da most Happy Christmas to you."

She watched the broad back and the big roan picking up into a gallop, and then he actually turned around in the saddle, took off his hat, and waved it at her from the distance.

Later that day, when Louisa and Rosa were having the late afternoon cup of tea while Mama was resting, they talked about what a happy Christmas they had and how nice it was to have Henry home and to have such a special guest. Rosa could not help but voice the thing she had been thinking about. "Well, Sister, I think that Mr. E.J. is kind of sweet on you. Maybe he will come callin' on you again."

Louisa broke out in a giggly laugh; then she reached over and hugged her little sister. "Oh, Rosa Ellen, Rosey, you really are such a baby. Mr. E.J. is not interested in me, although I would be mighty proud if he was, but he only has those green eyes on the lookout for one little gal, and that's you, little Rosey. You better look sharp or that big cowboy will steal you away." She laughed again and got up and went back to her work.

Rosa sat there and blushed all over. My goodness, could that be true, could that really be true? And a big flood of joy spread from her heart right down to her toes. Well, that was it then; maybe she was sweet on the big cowboy herself, and that's why she felt sad when she thought he was callin' on Louisa. This was a very strange feeling, to be sure, but who wouldn't like him? He was such a true gentleman, Mama liked him, she could tell, and Henry had said what a fine young man he was, and no matter that he was German. Her own grandpapa had been a fine German man, and for sure, that's why she felt that glow inside her whenever she saw him step down from the roan and smile at her in that certain way.

With all these thoughts running around in her head, she jumped up and ran as fast as she could up to the her hideaway place on the ridge. There was a cold wind blowing, but she didn't feel it. She looked out at the blue haze in the far distance and thought, "Just at this very minute, just now, my whole life will be different; everything from now on will be changed for Rosa Ellen Scott, a grown-up fifteen-year-old lady."

The first few months of 1911 were busy as usual. She was helping Miss Stanton at the school after class and still working for the store-keeper's family, and it made a full day by the time she had finished with her chores. Her time for thinking was on her trips back and forth riding her Kit horse. She would relax and let Kit's rolling gait soothe her. She often thought, "Yes, when I am riding you, Kit, my soul is soothed," and she would always send a heartfelt thank-you prayer to the Good Lord for her Kit, for her mama and family, for the good life on the Homestead, and then she would always tell the Lord, "Thank you for sending Mr. E.J. when I needed him, and maybe Lord, when he can, to come see us again."

The first day of April, the church was going to have an outing and a picnic, if the weather permitted. The ladies were all looking forward to a real social and planned just what goodies their picnic baskets would hold. Very early that very Sunday, Rosa was out in the barn finishing her chores when she heard that familiar horse pull up into the yard. She ran to the doorway, and sure enough, it was him. He stepped down off the roan, just as she remembered, and slapped his hat against his chaps.

"Mr. E.J.," she called, "how nice to see you again." He turned and smiled at her, and her heart made one giant thump inside her chest. *He is here.*

After a quick morning meal, he was asked to accompany them to church and then on to the picnic. He was apologetic about church, saying he had business in town for his boss, but he would ride out to the lake where the picnic would be held later on, if that would be alright.

Rosa harnessed up the team and drove the ladies into church with her Kit horse tied up to the back of the wagon. Mama had smiled at that, and during the service, she patted Rosa's hands so she would sit a little quieter, as Rosa was very fidgety it seemed.

There was a fairly large lake not far from town, and the townspeople often picnicked there. It seemed to be just an inlet from the big Snake River, but it was always called "the lake." The ladies spread their quilts on the new grass and started to unpack their baskets. Many happy children were running around playing and having a great, fun time.

Rosa saw him ride in and step down. He looked over the gathering and spotted the ladies. He came shyly over and joined them for a very nice picnic. "Oh, Miss Louisa," he said, "you cook like da angel."

As the afternoon went on, some young people came over and were introduced to Mr. E.J., and they invited them to go along on a boat ride on the lake. Rosa and Louisa and E.J. went with them over to a large boat tied up along the bank. There were plank seats, and the fellows helped the ladies to a seat. This end of the lake was filled with lily pads and water plants which were turning a pretty green. Some had lovely buds just starting to form. It was a beautiful day, and the sun was warm on their backs. The young man handling the oars was strong and was enjoying the company of the ladies who, he was sure, were admiring his strength. Another young man, sitting behind the rower, probably felt left out of all this admiration, so he got up and knelt on his plank seat, put his hands on each side of the boat and started to rock it back and forth. The girls giggled and looked at him, and he started rocking it harder and harder.

All of a sudden, Mr. E.J. straightened his shoulders and spoke up, "Nein, nein, not rock da boat; sit down, mister." His voice was clear and strong, but calm. The boy only laughed and said, "Oh, just giving the ladies a little thrill, that's all," and he kept on rocking the boat.

E.J. raised his voice to a pitch that was frightening, "Fool, stop, stop, you vil turn boat over; sit down or I trow you in und hold you under; now sit down." There was no mistaking the threat in that voice or in E.J.'s menacing scowl. The boy stopped his rocking immediately and said something aside to his companion, but Rosa heard it. He said, "That big dumb Kraut, who does he think he is?"

The rower got them pushed up onto the bank, and Mr. E.J. jumped out and pulled the boat further up onto the muddy bank. Then he reached out and helped each lady out carefully. When the lout who had caused the problem jumped out, he made some remark to E.J. E.J. stood close to him and said something very quietly to him. Then E.J. escorted Rosa and Louisa back to the picnic area. He tried to explain to them as best he could that no one could swim or even stay afloat in water with so many water plants. Those plants have long twisting roots, and a person would be just pulled down to drown, especially ladies in long skirts. "I am sorry to offend, but dat fool vould have dump all ladies in da vater. I vould not be able to svim in dat tangle of roots, und I am goot svimmer."

They left very soon for home, with Rosa riding Kit alongside E.J. Rosa was suddenly very shy being alone with him. She wondered why she would feel this way. They didn't talk, and Rosa let Kit out, and it felt so good just to be riding along with the big roan beside her. Then they walked the horses, and he asked how her schoolwork was doing. "Oh, I will graduate in two months, in June, and then I will be my teacher's helper. I am looking forward to being able to teach the little ones."

But she wanted to tell him that she admired the way he had handled the boating thing, so she said, "Mr. E.J., thank you for being so firm with that fellow in the boat. I can see where it was a dangerous thing for him to do, and well, well, it seems that you are around when some trouble is brewing up, and I am glad that you were here today."

When they rode into the yard at the Homestead he said, "I leave now, Miss Rose-ah, but I—vel, vel, may I call on you, Miss Rose-ah? Is dat alright?"

He held up his hand to help her down off Kit while holding her eyes with his. Suddenly she felt lost. Call on her? On her? Why, why she could not believe what she was hearing, "Call on you" meant only one thing, that he wanted to come courting her and then, then, maybe someday, he might actually ask her to marry him.

She stuttered in her amazement at this. "Why, why, well, oh my, I, well yes, yes, Mr. E.J., that would be very nice. Oh, but well you see, Mama, well Mama. . . ." He quickly interrupted her, "Oh yes, Miss Rose-ah, of certainty, to speak mit your mama, I vill, dat be proper, I know, und Henry too, ven I see him, and I tank you Miss Rose-ah."

He stepped closer and picked up her hand and held his lips against the back of it for a long time. She could feel the warmth of his lips even through her soft leather gloves.

Oh my, she was very flustered, but she remembered her manners and said very formally, "Thank you for asking, Mr. E.J. I would be honored to have you speak to Mama and Henry, and well, we would all like, very much, to have you visit us again real soon."

He was still holding her hand and looking into her eyes. "Miss Rose-ah, I vel, I, it vill be sometime ven I can come again, and I, vell, und now I say, auf wiederchen Miss Rose-ah."

He put the roan to a gallop up the lane, and then at the rise he stopped and quickly spun the big horse around to look back at her. He just sat there for some time, easily controlling the prancing horse; then he slowly raised his hat and waved it to her.

She quickly waved back, then watched him gallop on over the rise. She stood there a long time, until all the wispy puffs of dust from the horse's hoofs had wafted away on the breeze.

Then she picked up Kit's trailing reins and slowly led her into the barn. She methodically took off the saddle and curried the horse down as she always did. Her whole body was filled with such joy. She put her arms around the sleek warmth of Kit's neck and sobbed. "Oh Kit," she told her, "Oh Kit, this is just the kind of joy I felt when you arrived as my birthday present. Oh Kit, he wants to call on me, on me, on Rosa Ellen Scott."

She slowly walked up on the ridge to her hideaway place. She sat on her favorite slab of rock and looked far off into the distance. It was always blue and purple way out there. She sat and watched the clouds hanging over the two conical shaped mountains. He had come again, he had come to see them, and he said he wanted to "call on her," and that could only mean one thing in her world. Oh, that was grand, just grand. She hugged herself and rocked back and forth in her happiness.

The spring came and went. Rosa was excited about graduating from the 8th grade at Miss Stanton's school. There was a nice ceremony, and as there were three other girls also graduating, Miss Stanton and the students had planned a special program. Rosa was very, very proud of her little diploma that Miss Stanton ceremoniously handed her. She also knew her mama sitting there was about as proud as any mama could be. Rosa was the first one of her children to finish schooling, and with such high praise from her teacher, too. Later, when everyone was visiting together, Miss Stanton took Rosa aside and gave her a special graduation present. It was a small leather-bound volume of Henry Wadsworth Longfellow's poetry. It even had lovely gold lettering on it. Oh, she was pleased and so proud that her teacher had given her such a wonderful gift. She would cherish it always.

They drove home from the school with Henry driving the wagon. He had made a special trip home to be there for Rosa's graduation. He kept saying how proud he was of "his partner."

On the ride home, Rosa couldn't help but tell her mama, "Oh Mama, I was hoping that Mr. E.J. might be coming along for my Graduation Day. I am disappointed that he has not come to visit us."

Mama hugged Rosa to her shoulder and quietly told her, "Little Rosey, I know how you feel about Mr. E.J., and maybe someday he will visit again. But dear, maybe he won't. To tell you true, I think he must be in our country illegally. I have been thinking about it. He did not ever tell us his last name. He might be hiding, maybe because he does not have a legal visa to be in our country. Maybe he had to go on back to his own country already, back to Germany. I'm sorry, Rosey, you may not ever see him again. But we will pray for him, as I have been praying for him since that first night when he brought you and Kit home safe to us. You know, Rosey, it must be terrible to leave your country and all your family and all that is familiar, to live in a strange land and all by yourself. And really he is just a boy. Oh, he looks and sounds like a grown man, but he is just a boy. But I do think, Rosey, that when he can, and if he can, he will come to see us again. You see, I know, little Rosey, that you have a special place in his heart."

One late afternoon soon after her graduation, Rosa came riding up the road from town and, starting to turn into the lane of the homestead, she saw a buggy coming from the cabin. There were two men in it, and the driver was snapping up the horse as if he were in a great hurry.

As they passed Rosa, who had pulled Kit off to the side of the lane to let them pass, the driver touched his hat to her in greeting. Rosa recognized the Sheriff of the county, but the other man was a stranger. He looked like he didn't belong here. He was a tall, wiry, older man in a dark, dusty suit. She could see a small, neat mustache and a bowler hat that she knew meant "city man." Neither man smiled, they just hurried by her, and the Sheriff whipped up the horse to a faster gait once they reached the roadway.

Rosa touched Kit's sides, and Kit bolted fast toward the cabin. Rosa jumped down and ran over to the porch where Mama was standing. Louisa was there too, standing in the doorway. "Mama, what is it, what's wrong ?" Rosa called.

Mama sat down quickly in her porch rocker and reached for Rosa's hand. "Rosey, the Sheriff and that man came here looking for Mr. E.J. and, well, it was very upsetting. The Sheriff was nice and was questioning me about any German man being around here visiting us, and then that other fellow broke in and shouted at me.

"He said, 'We know that E.J. Miller has been seen with your family, and if you don't tell us where he's hiding, you could all go to jail. Tell her, Sheriff, we have a warrant right here. He is a wanted man, a desperate criminal, and . . . and . . . you better tell us where he is.'

"And then, Rosey," Mama continued, "the Sheriff stepped right between us and pushed that man back and spoke loudly, 'I will handle this, Kreuger; this is my jurisdiction and no one will talk to my people like that. Now go wait for me in the buggy, right now.'

"Oh, I could tell that the Sheriff was boiling mad and so could that man. So he went out and sat in the buggy, and then the Sheriff said to me,

'I want to apologize to you, Mrs. Scott. That was very rude of Mr. Kreuger to spout off like that, and I will sure-nuff have a word with him about making threats to my people. Now tell me again, when did you last see this Miller fellow?"'

Mama sighed and took a drink of the tea that Louisa had brought to her. "Well, I told the Sheriff about the picnic at the lake and how that fellow from town almost turned over the boat with all you girls in it, and how that Mr. E.J. made him stop, and that that was the last time we had seen the cowboy, and that we knew nothing about him at all. Then the Sheriff asked if I would get in touch with him if we ever happened to see Mr. E.J. around, and he apologized again, and he left hurriedly. I did not even get the chance to ask him what Mr. E.J. had done that was so terrible."

Mama seemed very upset and held her hands over her face for a few minutes and then said, "Oh, I don't know why people have to be so hateful. And I can't believe that nice young Mr. E.J. is any kind of a criminal. That Mr. Kreuger was German himself, I could tell. I wonder why he is hunting for Mr. E.J. I wonder what they will do to him. Oh, I just hope that he stays away from here, or they will catch him for sure. And you know what the strange thing is? That E.J.'s last name is Miller. Can you imagine that? My name was Miller, my own papa was a Miller, isn't that a strange thing?"

As soon as Mama was calmer and went back into the house, Rosa took Kit out to the barn and unsaddled her, then hurried through the rest of her chores for the evening, feeling numb and very frightened and crying inside.

Then she walked slowly up to her hideaway rock and watched the last of the color fade off into the far sky. She sat there a long time with a heavy pain in her breast. Oh, what could he have ever done to be a bad man? He seemed so kind, so good. Well, she would not believe any bad of him. He could not be a bad person. There was some kind of mistake, and she sat there a long time with big tears falling down her cheeks and her heart heavy as lead.

For the next few days things settled back to the old routine. And then, as Rosa rode out one early morning to go to her work at the storekeeper's home in town, she noticed buggy tracks turning off the packed roadway. She curiously followed them over a small rise and pulled Kit to a quick halt. Over by a rocky outcrop was a buggy with the horse tied to a scrub bush. She quickly looked around and suddenly was very angry. Someone could look right down on the Homestead from here. Oh, that made her boiling mad! It could only be that Kreuger man; he was spying on them.

She turned Kit, got back on the roadway, and rode fast into town. What could she do? Nothing at all. Yes, she could tell the Sheriff—no, she did not want to do that. Well, then there was really nothing she could do at all. Oh, she was fuming all the way but then thought that, really, the only thing she could do was pray. So she asked the Lord, "Please, Lord, please tell Mr. E.J. to go far, far away from here. He is not safe here. Tell him to go a long way from here." And she felt her heart would break.

In the following weeks, Rosa knew that someone was watching the Homestead. She also knew that the tall dark man in the city suit had followed her and Louisa into town. He was just hanging around, like a horsefly, she thought, just like a nagging big ol' black horsefly, buzzing and buzzing around the Scott family. Well he better not try to talk to her Mama any more, no sir, Rosa would do something terrible to him if he did.

CHAPTER EIGHT

Changes at the Homestead

FOR THE NEXT FEW MONTHS Rosa's life did not change too much. She was working for the storekeeper, taking care of his children, helping Miss Stanton at the school, and still doing all her usual tasks at the Homestead. The friendship between the staid schoolmistress and little tomboy Rosa became even closer. Rosa learned so much about the world from Miss Stanton. They would read from cover to cover the two newspapers that Miss Stanton received once a month and discuss the news in them.

She had not seen the tall dark man around, and she began to feel that he had gone away. Well, that was indeed a blessing, she thought.

Early that fall a letter was received from big sister Belle, who was still living back in Indiana. Her husband had been taken in an epidemic. Belle and her two boys would soon be on their way west by train. Of course the train fare had been arranged by brother Henry—kind, considerate, and helpful Henry. He had also planned for Belle to have a housekeeping job with a well-to-do family in Burley, Idaho, a town near Pocatello. But she could not keep her boys with her. Could her boys stay out at the Homestead with Mama and the girls until Belle could make arrangements for their care?

"Well, of course," Mama wrote back immediately, "of course the boys are welcome here, and we will look after them as long as need be."

Soon the two boys, age six and eight, came to live at the Homestead. They were sturdy, well-behaved boys, and Rosa was happy to have them there. They were both eager to learn and take over certain tasks from Rosa. When Henry had driven the boys out to the Homestead, he was able to stay a few days, so they all got busy and built a small lean-to for the boys to sleep in. It was just off the kitchen, and it would be warm for them.

So, with a full house, Mama was busy and happy, although her health was not too good. She kept having her "sick-spells," as she called them, and then would have to take to her bed for a few days. The "spells" seemed to come more often now, and Louisa and Rosa made sure that all the chores were taken care of. The boys were a big help, especially with the gardening chores.

Early the next spring, startling news came by letter from brother Henry. He was going to get married. He was bringing his new wife to the Homestead, and he would not be working for the railroad as telegraph operator anymore. He was going to be a full-time farmer now. Mama and the girls were not to worry—he would soon build a new house, so there would be room for everyone on the Homestead.

Well, the ladies were very, very excited about this unexpected change. Really, Henry had himself a bride! Well, they somehow never expected this. Mama would smile and tell them, "Well, I never. Henry married? Why, I thought poor Henry would be an old bachelor all his life. Well, I never! But I am so happy for Henry—he loves it here; he loves his Homestead; now he can stay here for good. Henry's dream has come true." But planning a new home—they all wondered how Henry would be able to afford this.

Oh, there was much activity to get ready for the new bride. Henry and his Blanche would arrive in June, so the garden must be planted well before that, and a lot of cleaning and polishing and planning must be done. There would also be the need for some new dresses to be stitched up. These would be needed for church, and surely for the special social that would be held to welcome the new bride into the community.

Oh, Rosa was truly pleased for Henry. He would have a wife, a helpmate, and be able to stay at the Homestead that he loved so much. But somehow this left her pretty sad too, and many times when the chores were done, Rosa would walk up to her hideaway and look out

94

over the sage to the purple mountains. Now it had been over a year, and no word from Mr. E.J. Well, he was not coming back—now she was sure. Her heart ached and just seemed to ache all the time. All the time there was that knotted pain in there just aching away.

Rosa and Miss Stanton were following the news about the problems in Europe, and war seemed a threat in those countries around Germany. Rosa wondered about E.J's feelings about his country. Maybe he had had to go back; maybe he was back in Germany now with his own family.

Then the day arrived. Rosa had been on the lookout for several days now, and there it was, a nice new wagon loaded down, pulled by two husky horses coming down the hill. Rosa jumped on Kit and rode out to meet them as fast as she could. She rode up to the wagon, and Henry was grinning broadly. "Rosey, Rosey, hello. And Rosey, this is Blanche. This is Mrs. Henry Scott."

Rosa leaned over, put out her hand, and shook the gloved hand of Blanche. She was a large-framed woman with a very ample bosom. She was wearing a fine, brown coat and a big, feathery hat. Rosa took one look at her face and felt her heart hit rock-bottom. She smiled, though, as she shook the hand, but thought, "Oh no, oh no, Henry, this is not the bride I wanted for you." Blanche's smile was not really a smile; it was kind of a forced smile. She had dark, brown hair in a big knot under her hat, and her features were rounded and plump, but there was a cold look in her eyes, a sharpness that Rosa felt was not a warmth at all.

"Welcome, welcome to the Homestead, Mrs. Scott," Rosa said very politely. "We have all been looking forward to your coming."

A voice said, "Thank you, Rosa Ellen, Henry has told me so much about you." It was just a voice, low and not unpleasant, and Rosa chided herself—now, Rosa, she is probably a very nice lady.

Blanche was welcomed heartily by Mama, Louisa, and the boys and was made comfortable with a nice cup of tea. That evening, after one of Louisa's fine suppers, they all sat around the table and talked. Henry told them that Blanche had been widowed for several years and had been willing to give up her home and move with him out to the Homestead. Henry had great plans to cultivate all his acreage now, put in more irrigation and build a new cabin near the stream. Blanche did not say much but seemed very content to let Henry expound on what they would do. She was dressed very smartly and had a handsome trunk with her, along with a whole wagonload of household things. Henry had brought lots and lots of much needed supplies too, for the Homestead.

But Rosa went to bed that night feeling lost and scared. This was a different kind of woman, not a warm, loving woman like Mama and her sisters. Rosa did not understand her at all. Well, maybe when they got to know her better.

In the following days, as everyone was getting Blanche settled in, Rosa felt more and more that she could never understand Henry's wife or really get to know her. She was so different from all her sisters, so different from sweet, helpful Louisa. Blanche seemed almost critical of everything. This was just not right, or that would not do, or we must do something about that, or oh my, I just cannot abide that. She was also very demanding of Henry, actually telling him what should be done, but he would just smile and agree with her. He seemed very happy. So, it appeared that this lady was going to run the household and the whole Homestead one way or the other. Mama was trying very hard to please Blanche, and Louisa fluttered around working very hard and doing every bit of the household work, all the cooking and cleaning and washings. Rosa was away every day at her work in town and at the school, but she could tell that things were not going too well at home.

It did not take Rosa long to realize that this was not good. Mama was not being treated very respectfully, and Louisa was doing all the work. Rosa pitched in when she came home and had finished her outside chores with the boys, but she was worried. Mama began to look somewhat peaked, so the girls insisted that she rest on her bed quite often.

Also, Blanche was not at all tolerant of the boys. They were very well-mannered boys but still boys, and they had to be reminded of their manners often. And Rosa did not care for the way that Blanche disciplined the little fellows. Rosa felt boys needed guidance and gentle reminders and not strict, harsh, direct orders.

In only one month, Rosa knew that this was not working out at all. Well, this was Henry's home, he had brought home a wife, that wife was Blanche, and she was taking over, which was her right, but she did not seem to want to take over any of the work that needed doing. That would not have been so bad, but she was so very critical of everyone and everything, and that made all of them very uncomfortable.

Rosa pondered how to make things better, but she really was at a loss to know what to do. Should she speak with Blanche? What would she say? Oh, Rosa was very worried.

One Saturday, Rosa was allowed to go home early from work. She had been watching the storekeeper's children. It was a cold afternoon; that strong, icy wind was blowing straight across the prairie country. Rosa bundled up, pulled her hat down tight, placed a thin scarf around her hat and tied it under her chin (Mama had told her that she would look much more ladylike with the scarf on). She let Kit out, and they were soon flying down the rutted road. Kit was so sure footed with her rocking gait that she just seemed to skim over the uneven roadway.

As they neared home where Rosa always looked down at the Homestead, she noticed one of the ladies hanging out washing on the clothesline behind the cabin. Well, she thought, this wind will dry that in a hurry. But as she drew closer, she could see that it was her mama out there.

Mama should not be out in this cold wind, and the more she thought about that, the more the anger rose in her throat. No, her mama should certainly not be out there doing that at all. She drew Kit to a sliding halt, jumped down, dropped the reins near the water trough, and ran out back to the clothesline. "Mama," she called, "Mama, let me do that. You should not be out in this cold—here let me take the basket." As she took the heavy basket from her mama, she felt the damp, icy coldness of her mama's hand, and this made her furious.

But she said quietly, "Come, Mama, let's go in for tea. This can be finished later," and she took her mama's arm and walked her back to the cabin. Once inside, Rosa noticed that Louisa was all elbow deep in the last of the canning of the winter beets: many steaming jars were set out on the table to cool. And there, in Mama's rocking chair, was Blanche, cozily rocking while thumbing through the *Sears Catalogue* in her lap.

Well, something snapped in Rosa. This was the very last straw. She held her breath for a moment so that she would not scream out what she felt, and when she did speak, her voice was low and almost menacing. "Blanche," she said, "there is still a basket of wet clothes to be hung out. It looks like Mama has been all day doing the washing, which she should not have been doing at all. You will have to finish the hanging, as it seems it's mostly your bed quilts left, and, and," her voice became much louder, "and Mama will not ever be doing washing again." Rosa knew that she almost shouted the word, "ever," but she didn't care, she just didn't care.

Blanche looked up sharply at Rosa and in a kind of whining voice said, "Oh no, I couldn't do that; I'm not used to the cold here. Louisa, go finish the hanging."

Rosa knew this was typical of Blanche, and that when Rosa was away all day, Blanche was always selfishly burdening Mama and Louisa. She couldn't help it, she straightened up as tall as she could stand, snatched off her hat in the heat of her anger and sputtered, "No, no, Blanche. Sister Louisa has been working at her canning all day, and it is a very tiresome task. Louisa will not finish the hanging, and as soon as I get Mama her tea, I am going out to help Henry and the boys finish the chores. So, you will finish the hanging yourself or you will have wet bedclothes tonight."

Well, that did it. But Blanche did sullenly go out to finish the hanging chore, and after that set-to, she created a thick atmosphere of open hostility. Oh, Blanche was nice enough to the ladies when Henry was present but even then just barely polite. Well, Rosa didn't care. How dare this woman, this lazy woman, take advantage of her sick mama and sister Louisa's sweet disposition? Just how dare she be that mean?

Rosa knew that everyone would do anything for Blanche just to keep Henry from being unhappy, but this was too much, and it had been going on too long. Now she must talk with Henry about this situation right away.

But the next day was Sunday, and there seemed no chance to get Henry off by himself. Mama said she did not feel up to the trip to town on the wagon, and Rosa decided she would like to stay home with her. But Rosa insisted that Louisa go to church with Henry and Blanche and the boys. Poor Louisa was home all week and always looked forward to the services and the visiting afterward. It was her only time to be with other people, and Rosa would not have her miss it. So they hurried to get ready and left, all bundled up against the chill wind.

Rosa and Mama read the special book in the Bible that Mama loved so much, and the two sat quietly with their mid-morning tea, enjoying the quiet.

Then Rosa spoke up and told her mama, "Mama, I am so sorry that I lost my temper yesterday, but Blanche is not fair to you and Louisa. She does not do her part for the Homestead; she does not do anything at all except complain and cause more work for everyone. She is almost mean to Louisa and the boys. But I am sorry I lost my good manners."

Her mama had tears in her eyes, and Rosa went to her and knelt down beside her rocker. And Mama said, "Oh, little Rose-bud, you really were not very mannerly," and then she smiled a little, "but anyway, I was very proud of you.

"But you see, Rosey, Blanche is Henry's wife. She has the right to have things done here her way. She just does not understand that everyone must share in the work to be done. She does not understand that at all; it is just not her way. Henry told me that Blanche's father was a wealthy farmer over in Washington State, and she was an only child. Her mama died when Blanche was very young. She was raised by servants all her life, and I guess she learned her ways from always having other people do her bidding. In a way, I can understand her. She married and did not have children, so she knows nothing of a family's love or the joy of caring for each other. I guess she was a widow for some time before she met Henry at a church gathering. But there is one good thing about Blanche, Rosey; it's that she loves farming. Well, of course if she does not have to do any of the manual work, she loves it. But you can see that she is proud of Henry for wanting his Homestead to become a grand farm someday, just like her papa's."

Mama sipped her tea and continued. "Blanche has a small monthly income now from the sale of her papa's farm, and Henry tells me that in two years' time she will receive the balance owed to her. It is then that they have planned to build their new home here and to make all the great improvements on the land that Henry has dreamed of. But until then, we must live under one roof, you see. So, Rosey, our Henry will be fulfilling his dream all within a few years and not struggle like he has been doing before. You know, I do think that Blanche is somewhat kind to Henry at times. She does praise his diligent work, which pleases him. And Rosa, I think Henry is very happy; he does not see how cruel and selfish Blanche is to the rest of us. So, I guess for his sake, we will have to make the best of what is handed us; we will have to just 'make-do.'"

Rosa thought long and hard about what her mama had told her that Sunday, and she vowed she would try to be mannerly to Blanche for Henry's sake. But underneath this vow was the knowledge that Blanche would never change, and she came to realize that the four women and the two boys living so close together here would never work at all, even for two years. Oh, how happy they would all be here working together if Blanche were more like sweet Louisa.

Rosa tried to think of any solution. Suppose she herself left? Oh no, that would not do. She would never leave Mama and Louisa to live like this. But no one was happy anymore. Louisa was working way too hard, she was not her old, happy, smiling self at all, and Mama was looking paler and taking to her bed more often these days. Rosa really didn't care that Blanche was now openly hostile to her, but it did put everyone else on edge.

Well, there was one solution. And that frightened her and left her sleepless every night. She would have to write to sister Belle, who had asked in one of her letters for Mama to come and live with her when Henry brought her boys to her in September.

Rosa had also spoken to the doctor in Springfield where she had taken her mama recently. He had told her that her mama should not do any heavy work or get chilled, as this would not help the kidney problems she suffered from. He said that he had done all he could for her, that maybe she should see another, more experienced, doctor about this malady.

Very soon a letter arrived from Belle, and she urged Rosa to convince Mama that she should come live with her in Burley when Henry brought her boys home. She had spoken to the new doctor in her town. He was a younger man, and he seemed to be well versed in this particular problem. He thought he could help their mama. Belle also had plenty to say about what Rosa and Louisa should do, "You both just come stay with me, too. There is plenty of work to be had here in Burley, and it's about time that you two young ladies got off that desolate homestead and lived near other people and started to have a decent social life of your own."

So Rosa took Mama aside and had a talk with her, "Mama, Louisa and I have been very worried about your health. We know you need to get to a regular doctor. Here is Belle's letter, and we think she is right. We must make a change now, and Belle said that maybe you could just come for a while until you feel better and—oh, Mama, don't cry! Mama, please, don't you see that we cannot live here anymore, Mama? Louisa and I must go, and Mama, you cannot stay. Now truthfully, Mama, you and I both know that we cannot live in the same house with Henry's wife, not for another month, and certainly not for two more years." There. She had said it and she felt better.

After a week of prayer and thought, Mama decided that Rosa and Louisa were right. Then a letter was sent off to sister Belle.

Oh my, Henry was terribly shocked at these plans and objected strongly. He was almost angry, and no one had ever seen Henry angry in his whole life. During many evening discussions about this, the ladies convinced Henry that this move was because of Mama's health. Maybe when she was better she could move back.

During the many supper discussions, Blanche was mostly silent, but one time Henry asked her what she thought of this. Blanche's polite answer was, "Well, I think they should do whatever they wish. We will miss them, of course, but we must all think of your mama's health."

Leaving the Homestead would be a very, very painful thing for the ladies, but oh, it was terribly heart-wrenching for Mama. They were all worried about her now; she seemed suddenly to be just wasting away, so frail and sad. They all did what they could to make this easier for her.

The move meant Rosa would have to leave this place she had come to love so much. They had all worked so hard here to make it a home. It was not fancy, but it was Their Homestead. How could Rosa leave the rolling grain fields, the far distances covered in that beautiful blue haze? And she would have to leave the dear friendship of Miss Stanton and her happy life helping in the school, but all this was nothing compared to the very worst heartache to face, for she would have to leave her Kit-horse behind.

What would her life be without the small buckskin mare with the rebel coat, who was her best friend? How could she go away and leave part of herself here? It did not seem possible that she could leave Kit. But Henry had made her a solemn promise: "Now, little Rosey, little sister, you are my partner, and you know that I will always care for your Kit. She will have a home here on the Homestead as long as she lives, or until you can take her to be with you. I will take extra good care of her, Rosey, I promise I will. She can just live out her days here nipping grass and getting her hay all winter in her snug barn. I promise, Rosey, don't be sad now. And you know, little sister, Belle is right; it is really time for you and Louisa to be seeing new places, doin' new things, and gettin' married soon. You are grown-up young ladies now, Rosey."

Rosa cried herself to sleep every night now. The heaviness in her heart was unbearable, and there was that other ache there, too. Henry had mentioned getting married someday, and that brought up the picture of the curly-bearded E.J. stepping down off the roan and smiling that secret smile at her just as he did every night in her dreams. Oh, where was he? She prayed he was safe.

About three days before they planned to leave, a young couple arrived in a small wagon. The young woman was Blanche's cousin. Blanche had written and asked her and her husband to come and work for her. They seemed very happy for this opportunity, and Louisa and Rosa were glad to show the girl what to do. Henry seemed pleased with this arrangement and told them that the fellow seemed like some good worker, too.

The day came when Henry carefully loaded up all the ladies' possessions and the two boys in the big farm wagon. He had insisted that he drive them all the way to Burley, to sister Belle's house. Rosa had always suspected that Henry had something to do with Belle being able to rent a sizable house, and she loved her brother all the more for his concern for his sisters. The trip was long and hard. It took two days so that Mama could have time to rest.

Burley, Idaho, was a pleasant town with lots of trees on a small river. Sister Belle was so completely overjoyed to have her boys and Mama and Rosa and Louisa coming to live with her. The three of them could not help but smile and be happy too.

Settling into Belle's home was easy. Belle had even lined up work for Louisa, starting immediately. Mama would be happy keeping up the home on the quiet street, only having to cook for the boys when Belle had to work late. There was a nice church down the street, and the quilting ladies had sent word that they would be eager to welcome a new member just as soon as she settled in.

Belle had found a housekeeping job for Louisa in town; a widower with two small children would be happy to hire her as a live-in. And Belle told Rosa that they would be able to find good work for her, too. She had spread the word with the ladies of the church and would continue to ask around.

CHAPTER NINE

The Lonely Nursemaid

ITHIN A MONTH, Rosa was offered work as a children's nurse-maid in a household in the town of Pocatello, some forty miles from Burley. This came through a member of the local church, and Rosa was very grateful to those kind folks. It sounded like nice work, being a live-in nursemaid for two small children. Oh, she hoped she would qualify.

My, how Rosa hated to be parted from her mama and the family, but Mama seemed to have settled into her new life pretty good. She looked and felt so much better. She had seen the doctor, and the medicines he gave her seemed to help a great deal. Well, Rosa thought, if Mama's health improves here, the move was worth it; I know how much she will always miss the Homestead, but this is best for her now.

She left sadly, with her one small satchel, and took the stage into Pocatello. Being alone on this trip did not bother her at all. She felt completely able to take care of herself. After all, she had ridden her Kit-horse alone all over the country for all those years. But oh my, how she missed her saucy little horse. This trip was made in tears, and she hardly saw any of the countryside.

A servant approached her at the stage station and took her to a very nice residential district and stopped behind a very imposing three-story home. Rosa had been looking at all the lovely houses and was astounded at the wealthy look of them and of the people on the streets. She had only seen pictures of places like this.

Rosa immediately liked the lady of the house and felt comfortable telling her of her qualification to care for children. She had a nice letter of recommendation from her teacher, Miss Stanton, and a letter from the storekeeper's wife. She knew that she was not really a skilled nursemaid, but she hoped that being sincere in wanting the work and loving children would help qualify her.

Rosa held her breath when the lady was quiet for some time. Then she smiled and said, "Rosa Ellen, I would like very much for you to join our staff." She pulled a rope bell by her small desk and told a servant to bring her children to her. They were two small boys, age three and five. They were lively looking fellows, and Rosa felt that she would enjoy caring for them.

This family seemed very, very wealthy to Rosa's standards. They even had a real telephone in the study. You just cranked it up, and you could actually talk to someone a long way away. Rosa knew about this invention, since she and Miss Stanton had discussed them and studied pictures in catalogues. Sometimes Rosa was asked to the telephone because the lady of the house would need to give Rosa instructions regarding the children. The Mr. and his wife owned and operated a big dry-goods store in Pocatello, so were away all day.

Rosa had full charge of the boys. She was to supervise them every minute. She ate with them in the kitchen, and she played with them, made sure their clothes were proper and clean at all times, made sure their nap time was used just for resting, and kept them on a very fixed schedule, as she had been instructed. She was teaching them to learn their numbers and letters, and she enjoyed that, as the boys were eager to learn.

She had a small attic room that was just fine. It was usually pretty cold, but there was a window that looked out on the back yards of two homes. There were lovely trees and flowering bushes and walkways bordered with flowers down there. At night she could see many lights and a big patch of starlit sky. Oh, but she was homesick for the far, sage-covered distances, for the Homestead, and so awful homesick for her own sweet little Kit-horse and for Mama. Then there was that ache, too, for a certain curly-headed, green-eyed cowboy.

Rosa settled into this new life but always felt so terribly alone. She was a servant, and that was alright, as the lady of the house was gracious, and Rosa liked taking care of the boys. She was having strange feelings of being caged up forever inside a house all the time, but she realized that this would take some time to get used to. The only respite from that caged feeling came when she would take the boys down the street to play in a pretty, little park.

It was almost four months before she felt she could ask for time off and was given three days. She wanted to make a trip to Burley to see Mama and be there for Louisa's wedding. It was great news that Louisa was going to marry Mr. Balding, the widower she had been working for. Everyone was so happy for Louisa.

Rosa was able to take a train to Burley, so the traveling time was not long, and she really enjoyed the train trip. She recalled the long train ride they had taken from Indiana, and the wonder at seeing so much of this grand country. She found her mama in fairly good health. She seemed much cheerier and very busy with her church work.

The wedding was a simple ceremony in the church. Rosa cried the whole time, she was so happy for sweet Louisa. She liked the big, kind gentleman Louisa was marrying. Harry Balding had been a widower for three years, trying to raise his two small boys with the help of house-keepers. He was some eight years older than Louisa and was a stonema-son by trade with a good, solid business. Louisa was a natural born homemaker and made a loving mother to Mr. Balding's children. They seem to respect her, and who wouldn't love sister Louisa? But she was also crying for herself. Her heart was aching, as it did continually now. She was absolutely sure that Mr. E.J. would never come back. She would never look into those eyes and lose herself. She would never feel that glow, just watching him step down off the big roan horse. She would never, ever see him again.

Rosa was still a small girl, only 5' 3" tall, very slight and wiry, but filling out in all the right places, it seemed. She tried to keep herself extremely tidy, as a lady should be. She was a fair seamstress and was glad her mama had insisted that she at least learn the basics of sewing. Her long, brown hair was always done up, either in a bun or braided in a neat coronet wound around her small head. As she was not out in the weather anymore, her skin took on the translucent glow she was born with, a natural peaches-and-cream look. Her startling, cornflower-blue eyes were the first thing anyone noticed, but she still had that overbite, and the white teeth always looked too large for her petite face. Her movements were always simple and graceful and very efficient. The children loved her calm temperament and were exceptionally well-behaved under her quiet guidance. Her real hold over them was the threat of, "Now, no story tonight, if you don't behave properly." She loved to read to them and told them many of her own dreamed up tales of cowboys riding the range, and they looked forward to these bedtime stories.

Rosa's only real pleasure came in the letters she received from her family and from Miss Stanton. Her sisters and brothers who still lived back in Indiana were good about answering her letters with all the news about their families. Kind Uncle Albert in Kansas and his brood always had exciting news about births and all the happenings of the horse farm. And there were always those faithful letters from brother Henry.

Henry told about the crops and the garden and the new fences and fields and all. Sometimes Henry would mention "Rosa's Root Cellar" as if it were a very special place. He told how he had added a new roof and how nice and cool the cellar always kept the supplies. When Rosa read this, she would feel that joy of accomplishment, and she liked to believe that "Rosa's Root Cellar" would be there forever.

Henry's letters did not say much about Blanche, only that she was well and that the cousin was very handy and the husband a good, steady worker. A new house had been built too, and Henry was very proud of that. He seemed so happy on his homestead, oh no, "farm," as Blanche wanted it to be called. Well, he was content, and that's all that mattered.

Henry always wrote about the Kit-horse, and Rosa always cried with longing to see her and pet her and ride her again. He said Kit was fat and sassy and that he liked to spend time with her. He said that she would just follow him around the fields when he was working, just like a little puppy. Oh, how Rosa missed the little horse, her friend, her only companion for so long! She often mused that she was riding Kit, and she could always lull herself to sleep feeling that single-footed gait. Oh, to be riding Kit across the sage-covered slopes again with just the hawks for company, the wind blowing her hair, the tough, old, scrawny jackrabbits scurrying across her path. Well, she sure didn't miss *those* critters at all.

Of course, Mama wrote regularly, and there were all those letters to answer. Her evenings after the boys were asleep were devoted to writing, or sometimes reading one of the fine leatherbound books from the household library. Her kerosene lamp would burn late into the night as she sat wrapped in a quilt, writing or reading about far away places.

She had been with this family for over a year when the lady of the house excitedly announced that her younger brother would be coming home from being away in school back East. He would be taking up residence with them, and there were many preparations the household must make before his arrival.

When the young man finally arrived, there were many receptions and parties. The house was very active, with the cook and the three servants busy from dawn till dark. Rosa must keep the boys ready and dressed properly to make an appearance at these functions whenever they were summoned. Rosa learned a lot about the social order expected of a servant. The lady of the house even took Rosa shopping and insisted she have a special nursemaid gown made up. She was to wear this when any guests were in the house. She was to bring the boys in and just wait there until the children were excused.

After about three months the household settled down, and Rosa became aware of the young brother Jeffry, lolling around in the kitchen quite often. He was really not interested in the boys but would often sit with them for a few minutes. She had never spoken more than a few words with him. He was a slender, almost girlish-looking fellow with a shock of blond hair always falling across his brow. He had a habit of brushing it out of his eyes that seemed very staged, Rosa thought. He certainly looked like his sister, but he had a rather haughty attitude that the lady did not have at all.

One day, when she was in the kitchen pantry, he came in behind her and put his arm around her shoulder, pulling her against him. She quickly stepped away and saw the smirk on his face. "Well, Rosa Ellen, are you afraid of me? My, my, I won't hurt you. I just wanted to give you a little squeeze. See, you might like it," and he reached for her again. She backed away in anger and knocked some packages off the shelf. "You think about it, Rosa, a little hug, maybe a little kiss would be very nice once in a while. Who knows, you might even get a fine present from me." Rosa hurried out of the pantry and up to the nursery, suddenly feeling panic. This was not right, she did not want him to touch her. How could he think that she would do that?

Several more times Mr. Jeffry cornered Rosa, but she got away, then decided that she had to say something. The next time she looked him right in the eye and said, "If you put your hand on me again, I will speak to Madam." He laughed a nasty laugh. "Why Rosa, she won't believe you, a servant. I can do anything I want, you see." And Rosa knew that this was true. The lady doted on her brother. She spoiled him all the time, and he could do no wrong in her eyes.

This cat and mouse game went on, and Rosa didn't know what she should do. Several times she heard someone outside her bedroom door and saw the knob turn, but she always kept it locked and a chair propped up by the knob. She was a little afraid, as many times she knew she was alone in this attic part of the house.

Rosa had become good friends with Minister Armstrong and his wife, in the church down the street. She finally had the courage to speak to Mrs. Armstrong about this problem, and her only suggestion was for Rosa to find other employment. Rosa realized that this was the only thing she could do. She hated to have to do this, but things were becoming unbearable. The brother did not work and was always hanging around the house, and he seemed to think this cat-and-mouse game with Rosa was very amusing.

Rosa heard of an opening very similar to the position she now held and quickly wrote a letter with her qualifications to the lady of that house. She was asked over to speak with her and was quickly hired to care for twin boys of five and a one-year-old baby boy. The lady seemed very pleasant, and Rosa found that the only other person living in the house beside the servants was an older lady who was the sister of the man of the house.

The only excuse she could give to her present employer was that she just needed a change. Madam was very upset, but she was probably aware of the situation because servants are fond of gossiping about every single happening in a household.

The new employer and household were very similar; they were pleasant people to work with. The twins were wild, but she knew she could handle them.

Her room was not as nice, but this home had a lovely garden where she could spend time with the boys. There was the old maid, Aunt Harrietta, and Rosa could not seem to make friends with her. The lady was not even civil to any of the servants. Oh dear, Rosa thought, this lady is so miserable, she seems to hate the world. I've been here over a month, and I have not once heard one kind word out of her. She hates children too, so I must keep them out of her way. Well, that's alright. It's much better than having Mr. Grab-Hands chasing me through the pantry every day.

Being a servant was not unpleasant to Rosa. She did love children. It was fun to teach the boys new ideas and to keep them busy and happy. The lady of this house was also a very kind person. There was only one small problem, and that was the sister's attitude. This sometimes angered Rosa, but she tried to keep a sense of humor about the way the sister would carry on.

Her one great despair was in not having her Kit-horse or being able to at least see her and touch her. Rosa tried and tried to think of a way that she could get Kit to Pocatello, to maybe stable her somewhere near. But after having the stable-boy inquire around, she soon realized that stabling her would be too costly, and she dared not ask the master of this house; she was just a servant, and servants certainly did not have their own private saddle horses, and anyway, when would she have time to be with Kit or to ride her? She was to be supervising the boys at all times. No, it was a silly dream and not possible. Oh, she might have somehow been able to arrange a trip to the homestead to see Kit, maybe for a day, but she would have to leave her, and that would only tear her heart in two again. No, she could not do that.

'Course, there was always that other great despair haunting her constantly. A big, green-eyed cowboy who was always riding in and out of her dreams.

Rosa settled in easily at her new work. She really liked the boys; the twins were a definite challenge, always lively and into some game between themselves, so she had to keep a close eye on them at all times. The one-year-old baby was a happy little fellow. Rosa became friends with the chatty cook and the other servants; they were kind and helpful. They would all laugh, many times, at the awful temper of the Old Maid, as they called her. Oh, she could be charming and nice any time her brother and wife were about, but look out for her any other time. And Rosa would think, Harrietta acts just like that Blanche did.

The man of this house had a fine horseless carriage. To Rosa it looked like any fancy buggy, but it made very strange noises and seemed to have a will of its own. It had to be steered very, very carefully, or it would just jump out of the ruts in the road and throw everyone around like a sack of beans. Rosa often got to ride in this horseless carriage, now being called an automobile, because the children loved it and were driven around as a treat at least once a week. Rosa did not like the thing at all. It just wheezed and chugged, and Rosa always thought it was so much more pleasurable to roll along in a neat buggy, pulled by the matched pair of carriage horses, prancing and strutting their stuff out front.

This household even had some of the first electrified lights but only in the parlor room. Rosa had read about the incandescent lamp and did think that this was a really marvelous invention. She stood in awe of the light it gave out every time she saw it. But the truly wonderful thing this home boasted was an indoor "lavatory." It had real plumbed-in running water. There was a big white porcelain tub with fancy claw feet, and the chamber pot had a chain you just yanked, after which the water came rushing through it from a tank up on the wall. Oh, this was a wonder indeed. And there were special squares of soft brown paper to use instead of a mail order catalogue. Now this was a treat indeed! She was often in this lavatory because she bathed the boys in the big tub regularly. But, of course, this lavatory, this *bath-room* they were calling it, was not used by any of the servants. The servants all used the outhouse, out in the back behind the trellised garden. They had chamber pots in their own rooms and used their own wash bowls for washin' up.

Late in the year of 1914 Rosa read where Germany had declared war on France. Where was Mr. E.J.? Oh, she wished she knew; was he back in his own homeland perhaps getting ready to go to war, or had they put him in a prison? She imagined so many things about where he could be and always felt the ache. But she would never see him again, of that she was sure.

There was a lot of talk about this impending upheaval in Europe. President Woodrow Wilson assured the American people that it was not their concern, that the United States of America would stay out of this conflict.

Her life in the household was one of strict routine. The twins were in school part of the day now, and Rosa had more time because of that. She became very good friends with Minister Armstrong and his wife, Dulcie. She would take the one small boy with her and donate what time she could to help the minister's wife with her charity work.

In the servant's quarters, they would all laugh together at the antics of Aunt Harrietta, who it seemed, had singled out Rosa for most of her tirades. Rosa was quick to mimic the nasty attitude of the sour old lady, and laughing with the other servants seemed to help her through the terrible scoldings and hateful remarks that she had to put up with many times a day. Sometimes Rosa would say to herself, "Well, at least she doesn't call me 'Skinny Scotty, the Rebel Brat.'"

The coming Christmas holidays would be a busy time for the household. There would be guests and family members arriving from the East. The house was being decorated from top to bottom for the festivities. Rosa and the boys were helping out—oh, the boys were ecstatic and really a handful, but it was a happy and cheerful time for everyone.

CHAPTER TEN

The Christmas Present, 1914

JUST FIVE DAYS BEFORE CHRISTMAS, Rosa was in the kitchen with the three boys. They were having fun helping to make Christmas cookies. Dough and flour were all over, but Cook said it was alright, as the boys were enjoying it so much. Rosa thought nothing of the front doorbell, as in this busy house, it seemed to be chiming often.

She was startled and looked up when the kitchen door was thrown open. Aunt Harrietta was glaring at Rosa, and she almost screeched out, "Well, Miss Rosa Ellen Scott, there is someone calling on you, and he's calling at the front door." And she quickly retreated.

Rosa was startled. Someone to see her? And at the front door? Oh my, who could that be? She hurriedly wiped her hands on her floury apron and looked at Cook. Cook nodded that yes, she would supervise the children.

Rosa hurried across the dining room and into the foyer, and there, standing just inside the front door, was a big man in a dark gray suit. He was holding his hat in both hands.

Rosa hesitated for only one moment, then quickly wrapped her hands in her apron to keep them from shaking. He was looking right at her, and she knew those eyes immediately.

This was Mr. E.J. Oh, could it be? Was he really there? Just standing there, all dressed like a stylish gentleman in his wool suit? A topcoat was draped over one arm, and his hands were twisting a homburg, but there was no black beard, no unruly curly hair, only short hair slicked back and a clean-shaven, handsome square face.

He spoke in the same deep voice she had heard in her dreams every night for the last three years. "Miss Scott, I hope not to intrude," and he stepped forward hesitantly. "How are you, Miss Scott? Vel, I hope. I, uh, your brother Henry sends his greetings to you."

Rosa wiped her hands again and wanted to run toward him, but she felt like she was in deep water, struggling against a current. She could not move, but she finally managed to say, "Mr. E.J., I, oh my, what a surprise to see you, and here in Pocatello. Oh, I am fine, thank you. I, oh, are Henry and his wife well?"

She managed to take a few steps forward but still could not believe he was actually standing there. He was just there, standing right there by the door with the sunlight shining through the windows on his browned face. Yes, he was really there; she was not dreaming. She looked up into those green eyes, and she knew they were telling her that everything was alright now, everyone was fine, the whole world was fine. It might have been a moment or an hour that her eyes were locked with his. She felt her knees go limp and thought she was sure enough falling over.

He cleared his throat and said quickly, as if he had practiced this speech, "Oh, brother is fine, Miss Scott, and yes, to speak with you I have come to Pocatello. May I call back if this time not opportune?"

Rosa started to say something, but she was interrupted by a loud harrumphing sound. Aunt Harrietta was still standing there and definitely meant to be heard. Rosa looked back at her and tried to collect herself and remember her manners. "Oh, oh, I'm sorry, I, ah, Miss Harrietta, may I present Mr. E.J.; Mr. E.J., this is Miss Harrietta Styvenson."

Miss Harrietta's face was set in one of her bitter looks, but Mr. E.J. approached her quickly, leaned over, raised her hand up to his lips, clicked his heels together and said, "Miss Styvenson, to make your acquaintance is indeed my pleasure." He dropped her hand and stepped back, smiling directly down at her.

Miss Harrietta actually looked shocked, then she even showed a slight smile and, very hesitantly for her, said, "Why, how do you do Mr. E.J." And with that, she hurried past Rosa and said to her in passing, "Now Rosa, you know you have work to do; don't be too long." Rosa was stunned. Miss Harrietta had never, ever, spoken to her in such a kind tone. She almost laughed.

She closed her eyes a moment, then quickly opened them. Yes, he was still there, smiling at her. After all this time, over three long years, there he was, just standing there looking so handsome! Her heart was aching and starting to do flip flops inside her chest. "Mr. E.J., I, well, I cannot believe that you are here; what are you doing here in Pocatello?"

"Miss Rosa," he said stepping closer. He picked up her hand and held it to his lips. "To see you I have come, of course; to speak with you I must," and he looked at her with a grin that told her how glad he was to see her.

Rosa was all flustered, but she knew that nothing could stop her from speaking to him in private, and she also knew that behind every door, one of the servants—and Harrietta too—was listening. She had to clear her throat to speak. "Mr. E.J., I, well, at two this afternoon, I put the boys down for their nap, and I will have an hour's free time then. Can you come back at two?"

"Ya, oh yes, Miss Scott. Yes, I vil be here at two sharp, und I come to kitchen entrance, so as not to shock da household." And she answered his grin with a trembling smile.

She closed the door behind his broad back and leaned against the door and sobbed openly, the tears flowing down her cheeks. She felt the knot around her heart slowly unwrap its stranglehold and the joy come rushing in. He was here; he had come to see her! He was here, and he was not a cowhand with a beard; he was a handsome, stylish European gentleman, and he was calling on Rosa Ellen Scott at two this very afternoon!

Needless to say, the servants were in an uproar. They had to know all about Rosa's gentleman caller. Rosa was in a complete state of panic for the next hours, but finally two p.m. arrived. The upstairs maid, Marissa, would check on the boys, who were supposed to be at their nap. Rosa had changed into a fresh shirtwaist and had time to brush and rebraid the wispy hair into its neat coil, but she didn't even know the girl who looked back at her from her mirror.

Of course Rosa answered the polite knock on the kitchen door, and there he was. Her heart went flip flop, flip flop again. She showed him out to the servants' porch that was really just a screened-in porch and very cold, but she knew this was the only place where they could speak in private.

E.J. stood close beside her and put her hand up to his lips. "Oh, Miss Rosa, Miss Rosa, dose blue eyes I have missed so much, but you, Liebchen, here you are, a grown-up lady. Oh vait, da cold," and he quickly took off his topcoat and wrapped it around her shoulders.

They sat on a padded bench that was against the wall, and he said, "Now, Miss Rosa, to tell you about E.J. I have come. I should have told you before but could not, and when I have told you all, and you have given it all much thinking, den I vil ask you to be my wife."

His look was very serious, then he saw the tears forming in her eyes. "Now, Miss Rosa, oh Liebchen, you just listen, den ve talk, alright?"

She nodded and was giddy and light-headed at what he had just said. Marry? Marry? Oh, she had not expected that—to be his wife—oh my, oh my.

He was saying earnestly to her, "Miss Rosa, I am Emil Julius Von-Mueller, but here in your country, I am E.J. Miller. Ven I look for you, I vent to Homestead, have long talk with Henry. I told him all about me und told him I vas going to find you and ask you to be my wife.

"Miss Rosa, I am so vedy sorry dat I not let you know vat happen to me. I am sorry dat I could not write for dese years. You remember da last time I see you, after da picnic? Vel, I turned da roan and vas coming back to tell you about E.J. but den decide dat not goot, dat I might put you und family in danger. Und Rosa, I did not have da right to ask you, to ask if I could call on you. I had no right because I vas vanted man, und I am still vanted man. But that day it just came out; I, vell, because I vanted to ask you so much, so I ask.

"Henry told me of dat Kreuger man bothering you ladies dat time, and I am vedy, vedy sorry about dat, but you see, I am not bad criminal; I never do anyting wrong; I am just hiding from my family. My father is, how you say? a fanatic man. He vants me back no matter vat, or he vants me shot. I know it terrible ting for a papa to do, but I am only von of sons to disobey him. Dat Kreuger vas sent to America to fint me und also to fint some odder young Germans in hiding. But my papa vould give special orders to Kreuger to eidder send me back in cuffs or just to shoot me. Kreuger is dat kind of man, I tink, who vould do just dat.

"As I told you, I am born in Stuttgart, Germany. I am tventy-vone years since last August. I am youngest of family of eight broders, two sisters. My broders now are high ranking military officers in Kaiser

Wilhelm's Elite Corps. Papa is brewer, owns many breweries, but vanted all his sons to be military officers. Dat vas his vish, und dey did as he said, all except me. Vhen I vas young boy, I vork in da breweries mit draft horses dat pull da beer wagons. Also, I vas studying to be tool and dye maker, a machinist. I vas apprenticed out at sixteen to study furder in America; den after two years study, I vas to go home und enter da Kaiser's army to help mit da var machines. Dey sent me to Philadelphia to study und to live mit da aunt. I started apprenticeship, und I liked da study, but I already knew dat I vould not continue mit vhat papa had planned for me. I vould not go back, to go into da German army as papa vanted. I decide not to go back to Germany ever again. I vould stay in America any vay I can. No matter vat my family, my papa vanted, I vould not go into da army. You see, I do not believe dat Kaiser is right to vant to conquer all da peoples; dey do not vant to be conquered."

As he continued, he could see that Rosa was shaking, and he put his arm around her shoulder to hold her tenderly against him.

"I must tell you all, Miss Rosa, everyting. During tree months in Philadelphia at da apprentice studies, I plan how I vould leave dere. It lucky I had money saved, und I study da maps und decide vhere vould be best place to hide. Den von night I just left; I vas sorry about da kindness of my aunt, but I could not leave her any vord; I just leave. I catch train going to da West. I do not stop till I get to da Dakotas. I found vork at some ranches dere, as I am goot mit da horses. You remember I tell you dat in my papa's breweries, ve kept many draft horses, und I like to learn about da care since very little. Caring for draft horse no difference dan care of goot saddle-horse. Also, because I know to do da horse-shoeing, so I find vork. Oh, I did have to learn da vestern riding, but dat vas no trouble. After bucking off so many times, even a dumkoff learns.

"Da ranchers vere mostly kint und did not ask about me und helped me learn more of da English, but you see, I could not stay vedy long at von place. I knew dat vedy soon, Papa und broders vould have people looking for me. Und now, I vould be in dis country as illegal. So you must understand, Miss Rosa, I am vanted by immigration und also very badly vanted by German government. My older broders are most powerful in da Kaiser's Elite Corps, und vould have many vays to look for me, und sending a man like Kreuger is just vat I tought dey vould do. At vat I have done, my papa must have da great anger. Dat dey have not found me, I am veddy, veddy lucky." He took her hand and held it gently and went on.

116

"I vould have been caught long time ago, if it not for one kind man. His name is Pete Darrell, und he is Sheriff in Tremonton, Utah. I came to know him, vell, because a rancher in Colorado sent me out to Utah to look up Sheriff Pete. It happen dat I vas vorking for dis rancher in Colorado, and dere vas flash-flooding in many arroyos vun time. I see small boy caught in bad current und I jump in, und ve vere swept vay, vay downstream, but finally, I got da boy out. I am veddy strong svimmer you see, learn as small boy. My broders just trew me into da river every chance dey get, and I had to svim or sink.

"Da Colorado rancher und all his family vere grateful, but I told dem I must move on, dat I vant to find job on ranch vay out furder West. I figure dey knew I vas running, und dey vere kint to send me, mit letter, to dere Uncle Pete in Utah. He did not ask questions eidder, but he is Sheriff, so he knew I vas in trouble. Sheriff Pete got me da job mit H.K. Wilie who has big ranch in Tremonton, Utah, und also da vone in Springfield, Idaho, near vhere you lived. I vorked on both ranches for Mr. Wilie since da four years now."

His voice was shaking, and he was quiet for a while, just looking at her. She understood that this was very difficult for him, but somehow she knew that he had rehearsed this many times over so that she would know just what had happened to him. He slowly continued.

"You remember da last time I see you, da picnic at da lake? Vell, right after dat, I receive vord from Sheriff Pete in Utah, dat inquiries vere made about a German man seen around Springfield. Dose boys probably had something to do mit dat. So, I had to leave right away. Sheriff Pete und Mr. Wilie decide I go back out to ranch in Utah; it is two day ride from Tremonton and remote country. I never left dere dese last tree years, until few days ago. You see, Germany has declared var, and I tink dat all Europe vill be fighting soon, and I tought it might be safe dat I come look for you, Miss Rosa. Oh, dere is still great problem; da United States Immigration looks for me, and if your America goes to var too, maybe dey tink I am spy. Also, I know dat my papa vill not give up trying to fint me, und I don't know vat vill happen to me if someone like Kreuger finds me, because I vil not go back.

"But, Liebchen, I had to come fint you. I vas sure you vould marry someone else already. I vent to Homestead and Henry told me you had not married und told me vhere you vork, so I come to fint you, so here I am.

But you see, I am only safe at da ranch, und I must get back to Utah vedy soon; I am foreman dere now.

"I am asking you to marry me, Liebchen, and go back to da ranch mit me as my wife. I love you since dat first time I saw you kneeling in da snow cutting up your skirt mit da hair falling arount your pretty face. No, no, now listen, I vil come back tomorrow for your answer. I vant you tink dis all over. I am vanted man; I should not be here; I should not ask you to go mit me. It is not right, Rosa, but I had to find you, to see if you might vant to be mit me. But, Rosa, you must understant, I vill not go back to Germany. Dey vil have to shoot first. I do not believe in Kaiser; I vil not follow him blindly as Papa and broders do. I vant to stay in America, Rosa; I vant you for my wife. Und someday, if dey let me, I vil become vedy proud citizen of dis United States of America."

He touched her cheek to brush away the tears, "Now, I go now, Rose-ah. Tomorrow, I come back for your answer." He stood and started to walk toward the screen door.

Rosa jumped up and took the heavy coat from her shoulders. "Mr. E.J," she whispered, "Mr. E.J., I, I, oh, your coat."

And no, there would be no waiting till tomorrow for her. She knew exactly what her answer would be. She stood close to him and looked up, and she could see that there were also tears in his eyes. Then she stood very tall and straight and looked straight into those eyes, and in a quiet voice, with tears streaming down her cheeks, she said, "Mr. E.J., Mr. E.J. Miller, Mr. Emil Julius Von-Mueller, I will be most proud to be your wife. I will go with you as soon as you wish, and, and oh, Mr. E.J, I am so happy that you came to find me. I was waiting. I was waiting and hoping and—"

He reached out and held her tenderly against him, his hand holding the back of her head softly against his chest. "Oh, Mein Liebchen, Mein Liebchen, are you sure, are you sure?"

Rosa looked up from the warmth of his arms and smiled through her tears. She was giddy with joy, "Yes, yes, I'm sure; I am very, very sure."

He just held her tightly for a while and then asked, "Can you leave in few days? Is dis possible? Und ve must fint someone to marry us, und dere is da license und, oh, Rosa, are you very, very sure? Is dis vat you truly vant?"

"Yes, oh yes, I do want to marry you, and I can leave; I will leave anytime you say, and I have a friend who is a minister. I will speak to him.

He and his wife will help us, I know. Can you come back after eight tonight? And in the meantime, I will speak to them."

He nodded numbly, still holding her, and she said, "I will make plans, and I will be ready, Mr. E.J. Miller, ready to become your wife before Christmas." She reached up and did not hesitate for a second, she just put her lips softly on his strong, firm mouth for a moment, then turned and hurried away through the kitchen door.

By that same afternoon, Rosa had sent a message to minister Armstrong. She had the stable boy run over with a note and told him to wait for an answer. Then she patiently waited until Mrs. Styvenson came home. She approached the madam in the foyer as she was taking off her coat and hat. "Ma'am, may I speak with you? It is of the utmost importance."

"Why alright, Rosa, come along," She moved into her study and sat behind her small desk. Rosa stood before her nervously. She hated to do this—madam was so good, had been so kind to her, but Rosa knew it must be done. She took a deep breath. "Ma'am, I, well, I am going to be married on Christmas Eve. I am so very, very sorry that I must leave you with such short notice, but I, well, my intended must get back to Utah immediately. I am very sorry, ma'am, I—"

Madam spoke up to stop the flood of Rosa's words. She knew Rosa was flustered, and she smiled. "Well, Rosa Ellen, this is not quite a surprise; I must confess Harrietta has already told me the news. As you know, the servants are buzzing about your young man coming in here and sweeping you completely off your feet. But, Rosa Ellen, I hope you realize what a serious decision you are making. You know it is just not right for you to jump into this so suddenly. My dear, what do you know of this man? And I understand, Rosa, that he is some kind of foreign person, a foreigner. Are you sure you want to rush into this?"

Rosa took a deep breath and answered slowly, "Yes, ma'am, he is from Europe, and he is a true gentleman, and I have known him almost four years, and my mama knows him and my brother Henry knows him, and has given us his blessing, and my sisters know him, and they all approve. And, ma'am, I think that I am the luckiest girl in the whole world that he has come for me, and I will be very, very proud to be his wife."

"Oh, I see," Madam sat back in her chair and smiled. "Well yes, alright then, Rosa, Mr. Styvenson will have your wages ready for you. Is it the twenty-third that will be your last day then?"

"Yes, ma'am, and I thank you for your understanding. And, ma'am, may I be so bold as to suggest that Marissa, the upstairs maid who has been with you so long, be considered as the boy's nursemaid? She reads and writes, and she loves the boys. They do mind her very well, and I think she would be very good."

Madam seemed to be thinking about this and then said, "Well alright, Rosa, I will consider Marissa; I will talk with her. It might be less disruptive for the boys, and most of the preparations are complete for the holidays. Yes, that might be the best thing." She looked at Rosa and continued, "I am very sorry to lose you, Rosa; you have been splendid with the boys. I must say their manners have certainly improved, and they are doing quite well in their schoolwork. So, Rosa, I will make sure that Mr. Styvenson adds a little something extra to your wage as a wedding present from us. If this is your decision, we all wish you great happiness."

Rosa was overwhelmed at this praise. She felt the tears well up and quickly curtsied to her. She said sincerely, "I thank you, ma'am, thank you very much. It has been my great pleasure to be in your employ and to care for your boys," and she hurried out.

Before dark that same day, the stable boy came running into the kitchen with an answer from the minister's wife, Dulcie. It read:

Rosa dear, what happy news. This must be the young cowboy you spoke of, and yes, the minister will be happy to perform your ceremony. We would like to have it right here in our home at seven p.m. on Christmas Eve, and yes, Rosa, you will be most welcome to come and stay the night before the ceremony. You will need a license three days before the wedding. Go to the city hall and apply for it. You just have time if you go for it tomorrow. And please come by and let us meet your intended.

Happy regards, Dulcie Armstrong

So, by eight p.m. when she expected Mr. E.J., her plans were complete. She could not believe how she had accomplished this, but it was done. In one day, in one single day, he had come to get her, and in four more days she would be his wife. Her life had taken a very, very different path than when she awoke this morning. Oh, Mama, she thought, Mama, now I am going to set my feet upon a new and glorious unventured path!

At exactly eight p.m., E.J. knocked on the kitchen door. Rosa flew out excitedly and tried to tell him all her news, but when she looked up at him standing there holding onto her hand, she almost fainted away. He put his arm tenderly around her shoulder and grinned broadly. "Oh, Mein Liebchen, this is happy day; I am one veddy lucky dutchman today."

She had only a short time to speak with him, so she quickly told him about the plans for the coming days. "Alright den," he told her, "I vill pick you up at eight a.m. tomorrow morning, and ve go to city hall and get license, and ve can stop by da minister's if you have da time. I vould not vant them to tink I vas not suitable for you. I vill be on best behavior." He grinned and hugged her to him.

That next morning it was softly snowing, and Rosa was sure she was walking on clouds. He helped her into a rented buggy and tucked the carriage throw around her. He just held her against him the whole way. Oh, she felt so grand as the horse trotted smartly out onto the snow-packed roadway. She glanced up at Mr. E.J., all dressed stylishly and handsome with his homburg cocked just so. He was smiling at her, and she had to gasp to catch her breath.

"Mr. E.J.," she finally said, "I have been meaning to compliment you on how grand your English is. It is miraculous how much it has improved."

"Oh, Miss Rosa, I have practice long und hard; da hands at da ranch are sick of my asking about da vords, so I do tank you vedy much. Mit your language, I feel more comfortable, und Liebchen, I tink from now on, I vill have my veddy own teacher."

"Oh, Mr. E.J., tell me please what Liebchen means," she asked. He held her closer and said, "Liebchen means sweetheart. Little Rosey, you are my little sweetheart, Mein Liebchen from now on."

They smiled at each other, and Rosa leaned against him thinking to herself, it is amazing; is this the cow hand she knew? Yes, he is the same but somehow different. Mama had said he has much intelligence, and he is a man now, even if only a few years older than I am, and he knows how to handle everything so easily and has such grand manners. Is this handsome man really going to be my husband? Rosa Ellen Scott's very own husband? Yes, it was so. He had come looking for her, he loved her, only her. Her heart was full with happiness, and she looked up at him and said, "Emil Julius, I love you with all my heart, and I was waiting for you, and I thank you for coming to find me, and I promise to make you a good wife."

During the signing at City Hall, they were both shaking. This was a very solemn, very important occasion. On the ride to the minister's home they just smiled into each other's eyes. There was much to talk over; but for now, just feeling the love was enough.

The short meeting with Minister Armstrong and his sweet wife was pleasant. Mr. E.J. was polite and very much at ease. Rosa knew his handsome appearance was a delight to them. "Why, Rosa Ellen," Dulcie exclaimed when she met him, "you told us Mr. E.J. was a cowboy," and everyone laughed. That he was a "foreigner," as Mrs. Styvenson had said with that distasteful sound in her voice, did not matter to these fine people. They were just extremely happy for two young people who cared for each other, starting a new life together.

They could not stay long, as Rosa had to get back to her duties, but Dulcie took Rosa aside and spoke to her. "Rosa dear, would it be alright if some of the ladies and I stitch up a new traveling suit for you? We could make a wedding dress, but as you will be traveling right after your wedding, we thought a nice, soft wool traveling suit would be so much more practicable for you. You know, with the four of us ladies sewing, we can quickly stitch up a gown in one day. I already have some blue wool, and we will find some white linen for the shirtwaist. May we do this, Rosa? We would consider it an honor to make it for you as a wedding present from all of us."

"Oh, Dulcie, oh, how wonderful; I had not even begun to think about what I should wear." Rosa again felt the tears. "Oh, how kind of you, that would be the sweetest wedding present I could ever hope for. Oh, thank you so very much."

Dulcie broke out in a broad grin. "Oh good, Rosa, we will have it ready for a fitting when you come back the day after tomorrow. It will be such fun, and to have your wedding here in our home on Christmas Eve is very special to us."

E.J. drove her the short way back, and she was in a sweet daze, just feeling his warm hand holding hers and feeling his strength against her shoulder. He helped her down from the buggy and opened the kitchen door and said, "Liebchen, I vill come for you Thursday, take you over to da minister's home." He held her gloved hand to his lips, and those green eyes were telling her secret things she had never, ever even dreamed of.

The household was really in an uproar now, with Rosa's unexpected plans and all the other busy projects that needed to be done for the coming family festivities. Then, early the next morning, a delivery boy pounded on the front door, announcing that he had a delivery to make for a Miss Rosa Ellen Scott. Again Aunt Harrietta had answered the door, as all the servants were busy—or, as Rosa supposed, she always wanted to see who was coming and going. Again she rushed into the kitchen where Rosa was giving the boys their morning porridge.

"Well, Miss Rosa Ellen Scott, there is a delivery for you at the front door." She said "front door" as if it were a terrible place.

Rosa was beyond anything but giddiness, and she just smiled sweetly and said, "Why thank you, Miss Harrietta, how nice of you to tell me." She hurried out to the foyer.

There, sitting on the floor, was the prettiest little trunk she had ever seen. It was wooden with a rounded top, and it had fancy leather strappings that were tooled with flowers. Rosa opened the small card attached to it and it read, *Merry Christmas to my lovely bride, with much love, E.J.*

This much joy is so hard to hold, she thought as she looked at this gift. How could he know she had nothing like this. Oh how thoughtful and kind of him to think of such a fine gift!

The trunk was small, so she picked it up with the handles on each side and carefully took it into the kitchen. Cook and the boys were beside themselves until she opened it, and then they were all surprised when she took out several tissue-wrapped packages. Rosa opened the smaller ones first, savoring the excitement. There was a small box of rose-scented sachet-powders in flowery sealed envelopes and a pretty jar of rose pomade. The label said it was a witch-hazel glycerine made with roses. The large parcel was unwrapped slowly, and oh, it was a heavy, navy blue wool coat with a cape-like thing over the shoulders, and it had a hood you could pull up with fur that went around the face. As she slipped the coat on, she felt regal, just like a queen. It was narrow at the waist and then flared out all the way to her ankles. Oh, there was something else in the trunk. She pulled out a pair of neat black boots lined inside and around the tops with fur. And yes, oh yes, they were a perfect fit. How did he know she would need all these things? Rosa just sat down with the lovely things in her lap and cried and laughed and cried some more.

She saw how bewildered the boys looked, staring at her, so she jumped up and hugged them, explaining that 'most all ladies cried when they were so happy. She hugged them again. Oh, she would miss these little fellows, and she knew that her leaving would be hard for them. However, what better time than Christmas? Their little minds were really on only one thing, and that was what that ol' St. Nicholas would leave for them under their Christmas tree.

Rosa was certainly not aware of what went on for the next two days. She was giddy and just went around smiling from ear to ear. She tried to tell Marissa some things about the care of the boys, but she was not sure just what she did tell her.

In her last evening at the household, Rosa happily sorted out her few things and carefully folded them to go into the trunk. There was a knock on her door, and she opened it to find Cook and Marissa and the downstairs maid, Clarabelle. They came in carrying a rather large parcel.

"Rosa, dear," Cook said, "we want to wish you much happiness. Oh, it is so romantic and so thrilling to see you swept away by this big, handsome stranger. We brought you a gift, but you must promise not to open this parcel until you get out to your new home." So they helped her put the big, flat package, wrapped in brown paper, down in the bottom of her trunk. Rosa thought it might be a couple of large bolts of cloth and was very touched by their kindness. She thanked each one and promised to write to them and tell them all about her new life out on the ranch in the wilds of Utah.

That night there was no sleep, just blissful anticipation in her heart. He was here and they would be married on Christmas Eve. This had happened to her! Her prayers were full of love—"Thank you, thank you, my sweet Lord. You answered my prayers, you sent him for me, you sent my love to me."

Promptly at nine the next morning, with all the servants waving to them, they drove off in the buggy over to the minister's home. The minister and his wife insisted that E.J. stay for coffee, and they all had a pleasant visit. E.J. told them something of the ranch in Utah where they would live. It was very large, thousands of acres. They ran cattle and were starting to raise the alfalfa in the river bottom meadows. E.J. was the foreman of the ranch, and with the owner there only occasionally, there were many duties to attend to. There were some ten hired cow hands, two Mexican families working on the ranch, and a blacksmith, whose wife was the ranch cook. There was a small cabin some distance from the main ranch house, and this would be their new home. "I know it not now much of a home, but I tink Rosa can fix up da cabin real nice. Dere needs da curtains and such, but it is snug and varm mit fine fireplace. In da summer dere are da hollyhocks and even da roses growing all around da cabin."

Rosa was, of course, hanging on every word and could see the cabin in her heart. She immediately thought of the song, "Little Church in the Wildwood," only this would be, "Little Cabin in the Wildwood."

Later that day the traveling suit was fitted, and Rosa was fussed over by five happy ladies. They sat and had tea and completed the finishing touches on the garments. Oh, it fit so well; there was the soft, woolen skirt with nice roomy pockets so she would not have to bother with a bag. The jacket was snug fitting with puffy sleeves at the shoulders and two rows of buttons marching down the front and buttons on the cuffs. There was a smartly-tailored shirtwaist of fine, white linen with sprigs of light blue flowers all over. Oh, she would look so special!

And the ladies were really excited when she showed them her new coat and boots. As if all this were not enough, the ladies spread out a pure white muslin gown on her lap. It had a shirred bodice and lace at the collar and around the sleeves. It was so soft it was breathtaking. These wonderful ladies were having such fun with these gifts and were being so kind, that she, of course, had to cry again. "Oh, I seem to be crying every few seconds," she said, and they smiled with her, sharing in her joy.

Later that afternoon, after bathing and drying her hair, the ladies helped her dress and do up her hair. It was not in its usual braid or bun, but waved with special curling irons kept hot on the stove. The waves fell softly down her back. They had managed to get two large ringlet curls on each side of her face, and they hung down the front of her shirtwaist. Then they tied a blue satin ribbon, tied with a huge bow, around her head to hold the hair in place. She had never, ever, felt so elegant and so ladylike.

At about six, when E.J. arrived, it was snowing just a little. As he stepped inside, his topcoat was covered with snowflakes. He was grinning, and Rosa smiled back with that lump of joy in her throat. Yes, he was here, this was not a dream.

He looked at her, and suddenly she felt like the most beautiful woman in the world. He handed her a small white box, and she gasped as she opened it. There were three white roses just starting to open, with a spray of baby's breath, all tied up with a white satin ribbon. Roses, real live white roses, and in the middle of winter, in Idaho? How could this be?

The simple ceremony was held in the minister's front parlor. There was the pretty Christmas tree, all decorated with flickering candles, many other soft candles glowed in the room, and there was a warm fire in the fireplace. The minister's wife stood up with Rosa, and the other ladies and their husbands were present. Rosa stood with her E.J just as proud and straight and tall as she could. She wore her lovely blue skirt with the soft shirtwaist and held onto the precious white roses ever so tenderly. Mr. E.J. even had a small gold wedding band to slip on her finger. She knew that only heaven could be this glorious.

After the ceremony there was laughing and hugging and many congratulations and hot tea and a pretty little cake to cut and enjoy. All these friends were very happy to be a part of this special occasion for Rosa and her handsome "Cavalier," as they called him.

About eight p.m. Mr. and Mrs. Miller took the buggy way uptown to a hotel where E.J. said he had made arrangements. The next morning they were going to take the train out of Pocatello, down to Burley where her mama and sisters lived. E.J. knew she would want to see her mama before they went on to Utah. Minister Armstrong had called on his telephone to the minister in Burley, hoping that word of their arrival might be received by her mama.

Rosa was way up there, walking on clouds. She did not feel strange, going into the big grand hotel; she was with her very own big, handsome husband. She sat in the decorated lobby while he signed in, and she knew she was now a grown-up lady.

Then he took her into the quiet, elegant dining room and proudly helped her remove her coat and politely sat her at the small table. There were candles and soft carpets, and all was very plush. She laid her roses carefully on the table, still marveling at them. Rosa wondered how Mr. E.J. could afford such a luxurious place and how he could spend all he had on these gifts for her, but then she thought that would not be a polite thing to ask your husband. Ladies would not ask about that.

She was so elated, just being across the table from this debonair husband of hers, that she did not even know what they ate. Whatever it was, it must have been delicious, and she really enjoyed the excellent service—like the waiter shaking out her napkin and laying it across her lap and then hovering around pouring more tea. "Is everything satisfactory, sir?" and so on, but she could not remember the food at all.

As he helped her up the stairway, down a hall, and opened the room, she began to shake all over. Oh, my, oh my, this is my wedding night, and I don't know what I am supposed to do.

E.J. hung her coat on the ornate coat-tree beside the door and told her, "Mrs. Miller, your trunk is right by da commode; I tink everyting you need is dere. Now, I vill step out for short while, alright?"

"Oh yes, Mr. Miller, that will be fine," she whispered, and he leaned down and kissed her cheek and went quietly out the door.

She looked around. Oh my, I guess I should wash up and put on my gown. She opened the cabinet below the wash basin and saw the china chamber-pot. Oh good, yes, there really is everything one would need. When she poured the water from the big pitcher into the china washbowl, she marvelled that it was actually warm—how lovely and how elegant. She folded her traveling suit very carefully and placed it in her trunk after she laid out the muslin gown the ladies had made for her. Oh, she loved the softness of the fine material against her skin. She looked at herself in the mirror. My, is that you, Rosa Ellen? Well you certainly don't look like "Skinny Scotty" anymore, and I don't know you at all. Her face was flushed, and there was a strange brightness in the blue eyes that looked back at her.

As she pulled down the big comforter on the bed, she noticed that the pillowslips had wide bands of lace. Oh, how pretty. She crawled into the big bed and sat with a pillow behind her back and looked over the room. A cozy fire was glowing in a fireplace; there was a small round table there by the fire and a chair. On the table was a stylish kerosene lamp with a red base. Oh! She jumped up. Her roses, she had left them on the table. She found a glass and put her small bouquet in water. Such tender, beautiful things, she had never seen anything so perfect, so lovely. She put the glass on the table and jumped back into the big, soft bed.

She had been trying to keep her mind on looking at the room, but it kept hopping right back—this was her "Wedding Night." She had heard all kinds of stories about wedding nights, but she still had no idea what would happen or what she was supposed to do. She fluffed out her hair; she had let it down around her shoulders, and she felt it falling softly around her face and knew that it looked very nice.

Then there was a slight knock and a click of a key in the lock. Her last thought was, "Oh, Mama, Mama, why didn't you tell me what to do on my wedding night?"

He came in smiling and stomped snow and brushed some flakes off his shoulders. "I took liddle valk, so lovely, vonderful night. Ah, I see you are comfy; I vil stoke up fire some." As he knelt to do this, he said, "Vell, Mrs. Miller, Mrs. E.J. Miller, here ve are, ve are married. Did you ever believe? In von veek, ve are da Mr. and Mrs.?" He was smiling at her tenderly, and he must have known how nervous she was, so he said, "I vil just turn down lamp some, dere."

She realized that he had moved the lamp over to the washstand, and she could hear the water being poured into the basin. Oh, she couldn't help it, she had to peek a little. She saw that he was shaving, with white lather on his face. He was using an ivory handled straight-razor with quick, sure movements. Then she noticed that he had no shirt on. The broad chest had black curling hair all over it, and there was even some of the same curly hair on his back. Oh, oh, oh my, she did not know that men had hair all over their body too. She closed her eyes and was a little frightened.

When she felt him lift back the covers, she opened her eyes and smiled shyly at him. She could see by the light from the fire that he had on a white nightshirt, and the buttoned opening at the neckline showed a wealth of that curly black hair.

He sat next to her and drew her over into his arms. "Oh Liebchen, mein liddle Rosey, as your mama calls you, you don't be afraid. Listen, our beginning is now; you are my wife, I love you veddy much. I guess I always love you, liddle Liebchen. Now, get comfy. Are you varm? dere," and he tucked the quilt up around her. "Dere now, ve are going to have long talk, den, Liebchen, to sleep you are going. Now, now, stop da shaking. It is alright now."

He started to tell her about the Utah ranch. "Yes, Rose-ah, it is remote from any ranch. Takes da two-day vagon drive from town of Tremonton, Utah, vich is nort da Salt Lake City und da great Salt Lake basin. Da ranch is in long, long valley, many, many miles long; da mountains on both sides are even part of da ranch, too. Dere small river running tru ranch, lots good grass for da grazing, und ve grow da alfalfa in meadows for da vinter feed. My boss, Mr. H.K. Wilie, is goot man; he does not come to ranch, only 'bout two times in da year. He is vealthy man; he has da plans to be da Senator from Idaho—imagine dat, a Senator of dese United States. He also has home in Boise, Idaho, und da big ranch in Springfield. Und how good it vas dat I vas sent dere to Springfield to vork dat time, else I vould never have found my Leibchen." He pulled her closer and held her head softly against his chest as carefully as if she might break. She was feeling almost faint from the scent of him, and the warmth that he exuded seemed to be pulling her deep inside him. Oh my, oh my, this must be what they call the "rapture of love" that I read about in poems.

He was telling her, "Vhen I first vent to da ranch in Utah, I vas da horse wrangler, caring for da horse remudas; den I vas sent to Springfield ranch to vork da horses dere. Mr. Wilie vas understanding dat I might be in troubles, so he sent me out to da Utah ranch und told me I vould be foreman dere. I was much surprised und proud to do dat. I make sure da ranch runs goot. Dere is much vork, but I have da fine hands. Mr. Wilie feeds his hands extra good, so da boys don't care dey so far from town. Dere is big main ranch house vhere ve all eat in da kitchen; dere are da bunkhouses, some cabins und lots of sheds, couple big barns, many da pen for chicken und pigs und cattle und horses, big garden, und orchard, too. I tink you vil like our cabin. It pretty in spring. I have not fixed up real fine; I tink maybe I not find you, or I find you married to someone, but I tink you can fix up real spiffy in no time. Now, I have tot of right saddle horse for you. I tink dere is bay mare dat be just right; she has two vhite stockings, she is vell-mannered. Vould you like her? I know she not as good a rider as your Kit mustang, but she be OK. Oh, did I not tell you dat I saw da Kit vhen I go to Henry's? Und you know, I tink she remember me. She nicker at me und come running like da dickens, und I have some good visit mit her. Oh Rosa, she fat und sassy. Und I know she misses you too, but Henry gives her good care. He spoils her, I could tell, und he spends lots of time vith her, her coat vas so shiny and clean. Do you think you vill like the bay mare Leibchen?"

"Oh yes, oh yes, Mr. E.J. Oh, I would like that very much," she managed to whisper against his broad chest. She was so enjoying the blissful warmth of him that was completely surrounding her, and oh how she loved hearing him tell her all these wonderful things.

He leaned his cheek on the top of her head and snuggled her over even closer to him and said, "Now, Mrs. Miller, Mrs. E.J. Miller, you drift to da sleep like da good liddle girl."

Rosa sighed and felt so warm and comfortable, just like a cherished lady, and then she thought to herself, "But wait, oh no, this can't be!" And she raised her head and said, "Oh no, Mr. E.J., this is not the way it's supposed to be; this is our wedding night. I, we, I, well, we are not supposed to just go to sleep; that won't do at all."

He threw back his head and chuckled and hugged her to him, "But, Rosa Ellen, I vant to be gentle for you und let you know me better."

She put her hands on his face and kissed him softly, then could not believe she did that, and suddenly she felt an urge just to kiss him all over, and that was a very frightening thought. She still held his face and looked at him. "But, Mr. E.J., Mr. Miller, I, I, well, I want to tell you, that I, well, I have never kissed a man, and, and I have never seen a man, and I, well, I—"

He stopped her with a kiss on her forehead and smiled broadly. The firelight was glowing in his eyes. Oh, she would always remember his face, strong and clean, looking down at her with such tenderness.

He put one hand gently on her shoulder, "Oh, Mein Liebchen, I know you have never been vith a man. I know little von, and dat is why I do not vant to frighten. Now, let me tell you someting about German boys," and he tucked her head under his chin.

"Vhen German boys are about fourteen, dere papas take dem to special lady's house. Da special lady teaches da boys about da coupling of man und woman. She teach how joyous it should be. She also teach dem how to keep dere own body pure for dere future as goot husbands und to make da fine sons. I know, little Rosey, dat dey do not teach boys anyting like dat here in America, und dey do not teach da girls much, I guess. Now, Rosey, tink about it, men are just liddle boys, growed up. I know you have change lots of da baby-boys didies, have you not?"

She giggled and nodded. "Vell den," he continued, "ve are all da same, you see. Now, you just close da eyes and ve sleep. It is enough for me now, just to holt you und know dat you are my wife. I still cannot believe dat you vait so long for dis dutchman. I love you, Mein Liebchen."

Again Rosa thought, "Oh no, this won't do at all; this is my special night, my Wedding Night." So she pressed against him and whispered, "But, but, Mr. E.J., this is our wedding night; this won't do at all. You have to show me what to do," and she felt herself lifting her face for a kiss.

"Oh, Liebchen," he groaned, "Oh, Mein Liebchen, to show you vhat to do vould be my pleasure, my greatest pleasure in dis whole vide vorld."

She woke about daybreak cradled in his arms. She looked at his face in sleep. He looks so young and innocent, she thought—yes, just like a little boy, and yet he is a man who carries a very heavy burden. This sweet man is my husband. My wedding night was so, so, oh, I did not know, I did not ever dream it would be that way. Oh, how I love you, my husband; I will remember my wedding night forever.

They realized they must hurry, as they had to catch the train very soon. There was a hurried breakfast in the hotel dining room and then a short buggy ride to the train station.

As they walked down the platform alongside the train, they followed the porter with her trunk and E.J.'s valise on his cart. Rosa was looking at the people already seated in the train. She was remembering how, as a little girl, she watched the ladies with the pretty hats passing by in the trains. Suddenly, she felt a terrible shock go right through her like a bolt of lightening. That face! that dark mustached face! She stumbled, and E.J. quickly held her arm more securely and helped her to hurry on. She felt herself walking, but a terrible panic welled up in her throat.

"E.J.," she whispered hoarsely without moving her head, "E.J., that man in the train, that man! That man is that Kreuger man I told you about! And, and I think he saw you! He was staring right at us!"

E.J. did not look around; he just kept steering her through the crowd, following the porter. "My Got! Are you sure, Rosa, are you sure? Und he did see me?"

"Yes, yes, I'm sure he did." He hurried her along for several more car lengths and said, "Here is our car. Rosa, listen carefully, stop here. Can you see him anywhere behind us?"

Rosa reached up to pull her fur hood closer around her face and shade it. She could see a lot of people moving about behind them. And yes, oh yes, back where she had seen the man, yes, she could now see him jumping down from the train and coming their way. "Yes, yes, he's coming, he's coming!"

"Now, Liepchen, please! please! It alright, just pretend I vas seeing you off. Here, take dese tickets. Quickly now, shake my hand und wave to me on da step. I vill lose him und catch up, or I fint you in Burley. No, no, please, Liepchen, it vill be alright, I know vat to do. Be my brave Liepchen—I'm so sorry, so sorry. Remember I alvays love you, Liepchen."

The porter helped her up on the train steps, and she turned and fluttered her hand at him. He waved, quickly backed away and was swallowed up in the people hurrying by.

She rushed to a seat by the window, but she could not catch a glimpse of him or that Kreuger man, just crowds of folks going by. She sat back and sobbed out loud. Oh no, no, no, how could this be happening to them? Then she felt a rage build inside her and become even more terrible than when those boys crippled her Kit. With that white-hot anger flushing all over her, she wanted to rush out, chase that Kreuger, and grab him by the neck. That horsefly! She would just squash him, and she stomped her heel back and forth like she was squashing a big, ugly bug.

She huddled into the corner by the window and held her hood over the side of her face. Other folks were seating themselves, and she didn't want to draw attention to herself. She looked down at the small white box she held. These were her precious roses, roses from her and E.J.'s wedding— was that just last evening? She started shivering all over. How could this be happening? Oh please, Lord, please take care of E.J.; we cannot lose each other now, oh please, Lord. She kept praying until the shaking subsided a little. Then she just sat there praying, and then again and again feeling the hatred—hatred for that awful man—and even feeling a great rage at E.J.'s father for being so cruel to his own son. She felt the tears on her face and angrily wiped them away.

The train made several jerky stops, and each time she looked and looked out the window and on the platforms of the small stations where they stopped. What would he do? What would happen to him? Oh, this was a terrible nightmare. Then for a long, long time she just closed her eyes and tried to keep the panic from taking hold of her.

At one jolting stop, the train huffed in the station for a long, long time. She looked at her small watch necklace and realized that the train was stopping at a siding for another train to go by. Oh, she was glad of that; this evidently was what they called the milk train, which stopped at each little station for passengers and freight. She looked out but did not see anyone at all.

After the train started again, she sat back, and wiped her teary eyes. Then something made her look up, and there he was, coming into the car. Oh, he was alright! There he was, just coming down the aisle to her. She reached out her hand to him, and as there was no place for him, she got up, and he led her back to the end of the car. He stood close to her, put his arm around her and held her close to him. She could feel the taut strength in her body. He quietly told her, "It's alright, Leipchen, it's alright now. I lost him. In Pocatello I lost him und hired da horse und rode hard und got here in time to catch train. Good ting it vas goot strong horse, cause he get da good, fast vork-out," and he tried to smile at her.

She clung to his arm and searched his face. She could see the strain and knew that he was making light of this serious thing. "Come," he said, "ve find seats; it's alright now, Liepchen, it alright, und I am so, so sorry dat he happen to spot me; just vone of dose crazy tings, I guess."

They just sat close together and looked into each other's eyes; there was nothing else in the world around them. She felt the warmth of his hand and his love encircling her like a warm, welcoming cloud. The fright and the panic eased ever so slightly. He was safe; the Lord had answered her prayers again.

They reached Burley within a short time, and there, waiting at the station, was Louisa's husband, Harry. He had come to fetch them in his wagon. When they got to the house, Rosa rushed through the door into her mama's arms. Mama took one long look at her and smiled. "Oh my little Rosey, my little Rosebud, look at you, just look at you. You look so stylish—oh, you have bloomed into that beautiful rose. I am so very happy for you and Mr. E.J. But Rosey, you look a little tired. Come sit with me; we'll go in the parlor and have a cup of tea, and you can tell me all about it. I want to hear everything."

Rosa was glad to be alone with Mama, as she could feel the tears welling up in her eyes. And there was that fear strangling her throat again. She could not help it—she burst out in tears, and her mama sat and held her head against her breast soothing her, making those hushing, shush-shush sounds like sister Belle always did when Rosa was a little bitty baby.

"Oh Rosey dear, what is it? What is it my child, what's wrong, dear?" And this question shocked Rosa into a sudden decision. No, oh no, much as she ached to tell her mama all about that awful man still chasing E.J., she couldn't burden Mama with this fear, with this awful fright. No, she could not dampen her mama's joy at Rosa's marriage and having them here for Christmas. Mama would only worry and worry, and they were safely here, so that's all that mattered.

Quickly, she wiped her eyes, put on a big silly grin and looked up at her mama's concerned face. "Oh Mama, Mama, nothing's wrong, everything is right. I am just so happy, so very happy, and I guess I am being just a silly, giddy girl. Oh Mama, I am so proud to be Mrs. E.J. Miller! Now, let's have our tea, and Mama, I want to tell you exactly what happened. Do you know what that Mr. Miller did? Well, it was five days before Christmas, and I was in the kitchen and . . ."

133

After Rosa had told Mama every detail of how Mr. E.J. came to find her and ask her to marry him, there was a bustle of excitement, and who should come bursting in the door, but Henry—dear, dear, brother Henry. He rushed to Rosa and hugged her so tight. "Oh Rosey, Rosey, we are so happy for you."

Her dream was now complete. Brother Henry was here. Oh, how happy she was to see him. Blanche was there, handing her coat to Belle and telling Rosa how happy she was for her marriage.

That Christmas Day of 1914, spent with her beloved E.J. and her family, was another precious memory. It was rowdy, with children all packed into Belle's cozy home. Sister Louisa looked very, very happy with a new baby boy bouncing on her hip. There was the hearty turkey supper, delicious pies, even a plum pudding with molasses syrup on top, that Mama served up. Then Mama smiled happily at Rosa when she saw Rosa's eyes light up at the sight of that plum pudding.

At the supper table, Rosa felt shy; she felt shy in a strange way. She was a married woman now, a different person. That was not a bad feeling though; it just made her proud. But there was that fear she felt every so often, almost a panic; then she would try to will that to stop. She kept glancing at E.J. He was so handsome, so confident, his white teeth flashing, his eyes almost glittering with the joy she knew he felt in the circle of this, his new family.

After the supper there was the caroling. Oh, how much Rosa had missed hearing her mama's sweet voice, just singing away at her daily chores. All the singing was jubilant, with everyone laughing and having fun. Rosa sang standing next to her E.J., his arm across her shoulder. With the warmth of his love surrounding her, she felt that even she could sing like an angel tonight. Everyone quieted when Mama stood and sang her own lilting Irish carols for them. And just before they all said goodnight, Mama asked E.J. to sing "Silent Night, Holy Night" for them, like he did at the Homestead years ago. "Come sing for us, E.J. We will all hum along with you."

He held tight to Rosa, and a hush fell over the family as he sang. Rosa knew that his heart was sick about what had just happened, and that he was homesick for his own family and knew he would never see any of them ever again. She ached for him. His deep baritone was strong and beautiful, but everyone felt the pathos and the heartache in his voice.

A small room was made ready for them, and they slept soundly, wrapped in each other's arms. Rosa asked him again what had happened in Pocatello, and he told her briefly, "Vell, Liebchen, I lead him on some goot chase. I pretend dat I not know he vas following. Den all I did vas disappear into da big boarding house like I live dere, and den I just slip out da back and vas gone. I rush over to livery und hire da goot strong horse. You see, it vas easy, veddy easy." But somehow, Rosa knew that it had not been that easy. She knew that something else had happened, something that had frightened even the big, tough cowboy, E.J. He had looked disheveled, his suit coat was muddy, and it had a tear in the shoulder seam. Somehow he did not have his topcoat and homburg. Well, he did have to ride a long way on horseback, and evidently he rode very fast and hard, and well, maybe that was it. But in her heart she knew that something very, very distressful had happened to him, but she also knew that now was not the time to ask him anything further.

Early the next morning they had to catch the train that would take them south, down into Utah, to Tremonton. This train ride was pleasant, and they enjoyed just sitting together and knowing that this was where they belonged. They did not talk very much. E.J. seemed to be very deep in thought, and she knew he needed this quiet time for himself as it had been a trying time for him. It was well after dark when they stepped down off the train at the small station in Tremonton, Utah.

At the hotel, E.J. told her he would go see if he could find his friend Sheriff Pete. He needed to speak with him, so she would have plenty of time to freshen up before supper. He held her close and kissed her hard, "Oh Liebchen, I am happy man. You vait for me, dose long years, you vait for me. For dis dutchman you vait. I cannot believe it yet."

He did find his friend, and Sheriff Pete was so elated at E.J.'s wedding news that nothing would do but that he take them to supper himself, and in Tremonton's finest establishment, too.

Rosa was surprised to see that Sheriff Pete was a much older man than she had pictured, with curly gray hair and a very stylish handlebar mustache. He had snappy blue eyes and a continual grin. He was tall and wiry, but he moved with a kind of fluid motion. Oh yes, Rosa thought, he is a good man, a very proud man, and I'll bet a very fine sheriff. She liked him immediately and had to stop herself from throwing her arms around him in gratitude for keeping E.J. so safe all these years.

Well, Pete was delighted that E.J. had found her and married her. He kept teasing E.J. the whole evening. "I kept tellin' you, you big galoot, that you would find her, but I bet this pretty little gal sure could ha' done better than waitin' for you, you big ugly dutchman, and it's a dern good thing that I didn't see her first," and so on.

Rosa laughed with them and enjoyed her supper. It was served very nicely and was tasty. As they were finishing their pie and coffee, Pete said, "I've been thinkin' about a weddin' present for you two. Now, have you had any pitchers took yet? You know, weddin' pitchers? No? Well come on; we'll sure see about that."

He hurried them across a street and pounded on a door. "Hey up there, Franklin, come on down, open up. This here is Sheriff Darrell. I need you to open up this here photography shop."

Soon Rosa was sitting on a stiff-backed chair, getting her picture taken. "I'll have to take two separate pictures," the nice old man told them. "You should have a close-up picture of this pretty lass. So, I'll have to take one of her and another one of the lucky galoot. Now hold real still, little lady. My, my, you surely have the sky blue eyes. I sure wish my picture would show those off."

Then he made E.J. sit very still while he went through all his motions and slid big wooden plate-like things into his camera, then covered his head with a cloth and said, "Come on, you lucky bridegroom. Don't move now, sit very still. No, you have to stop grinnin', just a little smile and hold it." Rosa was very impressed with the photography procedure; she had never had her picture "took."

Pete told them he would make sure they got their weddin' pitchers. He would bring them out to the Ranch himself, "But not till the spring thaw, no siree, not till spring." (See pages 138 and 139 for Sheriff Pete's "weddin' pitchers.")

The next morning she woke as E.J. was coming back into the hotel room. "Oh, Mr. Miller," she cried out when she saw him, "look at you, you are my handsome cowboy again." He was decked out in all his working gear, carrying a heavy sheepskin long coat.

"Up, up, Mrs. Miller. Yes, now I am da cowhand," and he smiled at her. "And don't forget, I am da big tough foreman, da boss, so you best jump out of dat varm bed qvick." Then his voice turned serious, "I've been to da livery, Rosa, make sure da loaded vagon and da mules are ready; ve leave right after breakfast. Now, do you have some good varm tings to vear? Da veather not good. Ve must get to halfway ranch before dark. Up, up, Liebchen, ve have vays to go today." He kissed her soundly and hurried out.

Rosa did have a heavy woolen gown, but first she pulled on her warmest undergarments, then the gown, then a heavy knitted long sweater. She would top it all with her new wool coat and a heavy muffler. With thick woolen stockings and her new fur-lined boots, she should be nice and cozy. She quickly braided her long brown hair and wrapped the braid around her head using her long, heavy pins to hold it in place. She folded her things and carefully placed them in her trunk. She looked at the single, white rose and again saw her mama's face when Rosa had insisted that Mama keep two of the roses, to enjoy them as they continued to open and become more beautiful. She knew how much her mama loved any flower, and especially roses. And she knew that it was special for Mama to be able to look at those perfect white roses from Rosa's wedding. Well, she would just place her one rose between two squares of the brown paper from the commode and press it in the small Bible she was carrying in her trunk. Well, she was ready now—ready to go to her new home with her husband.

After a hearty meal of ham and flapjacks, he took her over to the livery stable and helped her up on a high wagon seat. It was a large, heavy-laden farm wagon with tarps covering the load; the load was all tied down with ropes. "I vish you did not have to make trip in da middle of vinter, Mrs. Miller, but dere no other way. Ve must go now. I need to get da supplies to da ranch; dey are long overdue now. It vill be vedy hard ride for you; two full days in da open vagon. I vould not ask you to do dis, but I know you are hearty, a tough homesteader. Do you tink you vill be varm? It vill be veddy cold; look like da big storm brewing, too."

"Oh, Mr. Miller," she patted his arm, "I am not in the least afraid of a wagon ride, and you know that I was out in the worst blizzards in Idaho, riding all by myself. And even though that's been a few years ago, I am not afraid of the cold or a long wagon ride. I will be just fine. Now let's get going out to our new home."

Rosa Ellen, December 26, 1914

Emil Julius, December 26, 1914

CHAPTER ELEVEN

The Utah Ranch

THE EARLY MORNING WAS OVERCAST when they left Tremonton for the Ranch. Heavy gray thunderheads billowed high up in the sky across the valley. On the far skyline, Rosa could see the outline of some big mountains, all blue and deep purple in the distance with threatening clouds hanging heavy around their tops.

E.J. expertly maneuvered the mules and the big wagon through the few streets of Tremonton and told her, "Dis part of Utah has da many big valleys, many miles across, mit da streams running tru, und you alvays see da mountains on each side da valleys. Now, our vay vill take us up dis valley, den across a pass. See dere in distance, dere is da break in mountains? Dat da first pass, den ve go tru anoder valley, larger dan dis one, and den across anoder pass tru anoder mountain. Da ranch is dere in da third valley. It full two days, maybe more, mit da loaded vagon, so ve cannot dilly-dally arount und look at scenery," and he smiled at her.

The two mules were dark brown and great, huge fellows. Rosa commented on how big they were, almost as big as the work horses that her Uncle Albert raised back in Nebraska. "Oh yes," he told her, "Brownie and Blue, vedy powerful, ve breed dem at ranch and train dem goot. Dey pull anyting, but dey are da stubborn critters. Ol' Blue dere is vorst; he alvays tryin' my patience."

The ride was easy going most of that morning because it was a well used wagon road. There were many ranchhouses and barns and fields along the way. It was cold, but there was no snow on the ground. E.J. told her that she must remember, all during the trip, to stomp her feet often, to try to move about, as cold can creep in fast. She must keep circulation going so she wouldn't feel the cold so much. "Pretend you do da dancin'. I bet you fine dancer, Miss Rosa. Sometime ve vill dance together; ve vill be finest couple on any floor." And he threw back his head and started to sing a catchy tune. She tapped her feet, and they laughed as she pretended to be dancing.

Just after nightfall, they reached the stop-over ranch. An icy, biting wind and the continual jolting of the wagon made Rosa realize that she had been getting very soft working for two years in the comfortable households of Pocatello. She was almost light-headed from weariness. Oh, she was so glad to step down from the wagon and enter into a warm kitchen.

The rancher's wife, Mrs. Culpepper, was in awe of Rosa. "Oh, Mr. E.J," she cried when she helped Rosa off with her coat, "you never said, you never told us, what a pretty little angel she is, and for her to come out here in this country, in the dead of winter with you, you big oaf—well, I never—and you told us she was a homesteader, and here she is a stylish city lady. But E. J., I must say you do look considerable better without that beard. And you are one lucky cowpoke, but you better look out for me if you don't take good care of this here little one."

Rosa was pampered and fussed over. Mrs. Culpepper was a big, stout woman with lots of wispy gray hair falling out of her bun. Her white apron covered her ample bosom, and she laughed with her whole body. Her husband was another one of those tall, stringy men with hunched shoulders, and he had a most kind face under his furry mustache.

There was a hearty supper of steak and gravy and fried potatoes. Rosa put away so much food that they all teased her. During the meal, Rosa could tell by the talk that these people held Mr. E.J. in high regard, and that made her very proud.

They had to be away before dawn. As they were outside in the near darkness, Mrs. Culpepper started whispering to E.J., and then she grinned at Rosa and told her, "Well, Mrs. Miller, Jake and I have a weddin' present for you." Mr. Culpepper hurried back into the barn and came out with a small brown puppy-dog in his arms. He laid the soft bundle in Rosa's arms. "This here is a real cattle dog, Mrs. Miller, and he's gonna be real smart. Do you like him?"

Rosa was overwhelmed. A puppy, for her, a perky little puppy with floppy ears and white paws. Oh, what could she say to these kind folks? She could not find words, just nodded and held the dear little thing close to her and felt the tears running down her cheeks. Oh dear, I'm crying again, but there is so much happiness around me, I just can't help it.

Mr. Culpepper was saying, "Well you surely are welcome; he will make you a fine dog, Mrs. Miller. Now, my wife thinks you better take along another quilt and this heavy tarp to wrap up in. She's afraid a little thing like you might get too cold out there. E.J., it sure looks mean. Some real bad weather brewin' today. You better hump up those mules all the way."

E.J. wrapped the big quilt around Rosa's back. The puppy was curled up in her lap, so he wrapped it completely around them both. She smiled and waved good-by as they moved down the lane.

Rosa looked out at the threatening sky. It was almost dawn, but only very faint color in the east to prove it. The heavy, ominous clouds were now hanging near the ground as far as you could see. E.J. snapped up the mules, who were evidently reluctant to leave a warm barn, but he soon put them into a steady ground-eating trot. Going up through the pass, the way was not steep, just a long, gradual sloping up and up, and then down and down again, for many miles. In the next valley the wind picked up.

They stopped briefly about noontime. E.J. gave the mules a large ration of oats in their feedbags. These attached over the mules' heads, and they knew just how to push the bag to the ground and get a big mouthful of oats, then lift their heads and chew it all up with evident satisfaction.

There was hot tea made on the little kerosene heater and food sent along by Mrs. Culpepper, and walking around felt good. I just hate these skirts, Rosa thought, as she went around the wagon to relieve herself. It was so difficult, but thank goodness for buttoned openings in the long underwear, and the skirt did hide any soft skin from the harsh wind. She thought that she had been pretty smart to have saved some of those squares of soft brown paper which had been in the hotel commode. She had safely tucked them into her skirt pocket. The puppy had been jumping round the wagon but stayed very close to Rosa.

As the afternoon progressed, the wind became stronger and was now laden with big, dry snowflakes. The wagon was jolting hard along the roadway, and Rosa could tell that the road was frozen solid. E.J. had draped the big tarp all around Rosa and her puppy and reminded her that she would need to stomp her feet and move her hands very often now. "Do your dancin', liddle Liebchen, you'll need to keep dancin' all da time now."

In a matter of minutes the wind became a blizzard. Rosa knew the difference—she huddled down with her head and face completely covered under the tarp. She could hear E.J. talking to the mules, urging them along, talking to them as if he were right out there in the harness with them. She peeped out and could not see the road or trees or mountains or anything. It was all just a swirling mass of white.

It seemed they traveled many, many hours, but she knew it was probably only late afternoon. Every once in a while, E.J. would pat her and ask if she was alright. She wondered how E.J. could stand the icy wind and the deadening cold. She knew that he had thick gloves, and that heavy sheepskin coat must be extra warm. He had his muffler tied around his head and neck, and over that the wide-brimmed stetson was pulled down tight, held on with a strap going under his chin. Also she felt his working with the reins and the whip probably would help to keep him warm.

She knew it was below freezing. This must be one of those freak blizzards that moves down from the north country and sweeps like thunder across the land. She moved her hands and feet and body as much as she could, and the puppy would move and whimper in her lap. She remembered a blizzard one winter that came up suddenly as she was riding her Kit-horse. On her way home from school in Springfield one late afternoon, there was suddenly nothing but white. She could not tell the ground from the sky, and she remembered stories of how people got mixed up and went round and round in circles until they froze to death in such a terrible blizzard. She had been scared, but then she had remembered what her brother Henry had told her: "Rosa, if you ever get lost, you just let Kit have her head. She will know, better than you, how to get you home straight as an arrow." Well, she had done just that, and her little mustang had plowed through the deepening snow with those tough little legs and walked Rosa right up to her own barn door. Rosa had closed her eyes the whole way, because just seeing the swirling whiteness around her was so very frightening.

Now they were in a much more severe blizzard, but those mules were not hesitating; they were on their way home and seemed to know exactly where to go. Well, mules must be just as smart as horses are, she thought.

She could tell they were pulling a hill now. This must be the last pass. Then, after a long while, they did start to descend slowly. She was afraid of the cold now, for she could not feel her feet and legs at all. But she just kept up the dancin', and clenched and unclenched her hands, while she huddled down holding onto the seat. She knew that her hands and feet could freeze quickly in this biting cold and sent up a long, serious prayer to the Good Lord above.

The wagon was shuddering now, and she really had to hold on. She could tell that the mules were lunging through snow drifts. Then, oh dear, now what—the wagon had jolted to a dead stop.

She could hear E.J. shouting over the wind. She lifted a corner of the tarp and tried to see through the swirling snow. She could see that E.J. had jumped down alongside the mules, and he was whipping one of them who was just lying down, just lying there like a big lump in the snow. The other mule was lunging frantically against his harness. E.J. reached in under the wagon seat and pulled out an iron chain and swung it against the rump of the mule. He kept beating that mule on his big rump, and Rosa could hear a thud and another thud, with the rattle of the chain, and each time the mule let out a loud grunt. "Oh no, E.J., don't beat the mule, don't beat him like that, oh no, stop, stop," she cried out. But of course he could not hear her as he was so intent on making the mule get up. She covered her head and again huddled down under the tarp, almost crying to herself. He seemed like a mad man, so cruelly beating the mule; she was shivering and shivering, and not only from the icy cold.

It seemed a long time before she felt him jump up onto the wagon seat, and the wagon bounced and started moving slowly. They seemed to be going ever so slow, and she was sure she would be frozen stone cold any minute now. She was feeling dizzy and kind of sleepy. Oh, how easy, just to nod off. But as she started to slip, the puppy struggled in her arms and made awful whimpering sounds. She calmed him and then tried to move her legs again.

Then the wagon jolted to a stop again, and she felt E.J. jump down off the wagon. Oh dear, did the mule lie down again? Then she felt the wagon move again. She looked out from under the tarp and saw a light. E.J. had lit a lantern, and she could see that they were in a huge barn. Lots of horses and mules were stabled along each side. It seemed that each one was neighing or braying in welcome.

E.J. reached up, threw back the big tarp saying, "I am sorry, Leibchen, dis da fierce blizzard, but it alright now. Rosa, come quickly, I get you to da ranch kitchen, it be varm dere."

He actually picked her up in his arms, blanket, puppy and all, and carried her back out into the blizzard, evidently across a yard—although she could not see anything but white—then up a couple of steps and across a porch. He kicked open a door into a warm room. A kerosene lamp hanging over a very long table was streaming welcoming light. He sat her on her feet beside a huge black cookstove and helped her put the puppy down. He looked at her, and she could see the concern in his eyes. His face looked drawn and tired. "Oh Liebchen, I am sorry, so very bad da storm; here sit by stove, varm yourself. Ve must tend to feet, dey maybe frostbit, and oh, goot, here is still hot coffee. Are you alright?"

"I think—I think I am alright, Mr. Miller," she managed to say hoarsely, and she reached out her hands to the welcoming warmth.

"Now, Liebchen, you vill rub hands, feet, legs good; let me pull boots. You do dat now, just rub feet good und drink coffee, dat vill help. I be back, soon as tend dose mules. I need to look to Ol' Blue. He vill have sore rump for long time. I had to make him get up; I had to, else ve all vould have froze-up right dere in da snow bank. Oh, I best take da pup to sleep in da barn, he used to dat. I vill take da biscuits, he vil like dat," and he reached up to a shelf above the warming oven of the stove and put three big biscuits in his pocket. Then he picked up the pup and tucked him under his great coat and turned to her again, "Dere now, pup vill be safe in barn, he used to barn. Da cook vould not like to find dog in her kitchen in morning. I be right back, Liebchen; you rub da feet good, ya?"

Later, after they had devoured big bowls of cornmeal mush that had been simmering on the back of the stove, they shared a very small bed in the room just off the kitchen. She snuggled down in his arms, still dressed, but he had told her she would be warmer that way. She could feel his warmth surrounding her as she drifted off into an exhausted sleep, thinking, "We surely must be safe from that awful man way out here; we must be safe now. Oh, this was some honeymoon, and certainly a honeymoon to remember."

When she woke, E.J. was gone, but she smelled the hot cup of coffee sitting on the small table beside the bed. Oh how welcome that first taste! My, she was stiff, and her arms and legs felt like sticks. Her hands were tingly, but her poor feet were hurting like anything. She rubbed them as hard as she could and found her boots and finally got those on. The air was cold as she used the welcome chamber pot in the small wash stand. And sitting right there was her small trunk. Oh, how kind of Mr. Miller; he must be the bravest, the most wonderful husband in the whole world. The water in the pitcher was cold, but she splashed some on her face and found her brush and brushed and rebraided her hair. She usually could braid it up in no time, and this morning she was anxious to get it done quickly. She found another gown and slipped into it.

She could hear many male voices in the kitchen, and as she opened the door, she saw about a dozen cowboys turn their eyes her way. Some were seated at the long table, others were just coming in. The big black wood stove had pots simmering and wonderful smells coming from the oven. On top of the stove was a big black griddle filled with brown griddle cakes. A large woman in a checkered apron was flipping them with one hand, and she was stirring something in a pot with the other. Rosa stepped further into the warm room and felt every pair of eyes on herself. She hesitated—oh my, oh my.

"Ah, here she is, E.J's bride," the cook roared. "Boys, meet Missus Miller. She came in through this awful blizzard and will you look at her? Just a little bitty thing. It's a wonder that blizzard didn't blow her straight through to Montana, ha, ha! But I can bet that big E.J. had a good holt on you, Missus Miller; he wasn't gonna let you loose, no siree. Now come right in, little Missus, set right down, grub is 'bout ready."

Rosa was pink with embarrassment at the cook's remarks and, of course, the direct gaze of all the cowhands, but she tried to smile as the men all stood and said, "Howdo, Ma'am, howdy Missus Miller," and they made room for her on the long bench. Just then, E.J. came through the door, looked around and grinned broadly, "Vell boys, did you all meet Missus Miller?"

For three more days the blizzard did not let up. E.J. and all the hands were out in the storm every day. They were very concerned about the stock, and there were many losses—some of the cattle simply froze in their tracks. "Worst blizzard since aught-nine," the cook told her several times.

E.J. and Rosa continued to sleep in the room off the kitchen for the time being, as E.J. said he didn't want Rosa out in this weather. Her toes had been frostbit but seemed to be improving every day. They were very painful for a long time, but she felt she had been lucky. That dancin' must have paid off.

Rosa was learning that the cook, Mrs. Commery, was a big teaser. Rosa could tell that underneath all that bluster, there was a warm, loving heart, and she really liked her. Rosa tried to be of help and was allowed to peel and chop and stir things, as did a kitchen helper, Luca, one of the Mexican women living on the ranch.

"Oh, you've got yourself a real man there," Mrs. Commery told her as they worked. "If I was a young'n again, I'd have chased off my Anthony and grabbed that big dutchman for myself. E.J. runs things here. He runs them real good, Missus. The hands jump when he says to, but they respect him. He always works hard 'nough for two men. The boss was real smart when he made E.J. foreman of this outfit." Rosa reveled in this kind of praise of her husband.

One evening Mrs. Commery told Rosa, "Tomorry, Missus, we go over to that rats' nest of a cabin and clean it good, and you can move in. It's not much, but I bet you can fix it real pretty."

Well, it really was not much, but to Rosa it was a beautiful, sturdy log cabin. It had a partition for the sleeping quarters, a nice iron cook-stove, a hoosier cabinet, no matter that the doors were missing. There were chunky handmade chairs and a small, thick table. "Oh, it is fine, Mrs. Commery, it is just fine," Rosa told her.

They cleaned and scrubbed, and then Mrs. Commery took Rosa down into the basement of the big ranch house. There they found some rolled up braided rag-rugs and some heavy material to use for curtains and such. They found some blue dishes with only a few chips, a big iron skillet, an iron stew pot, and most everything else she would need. Rosa was elated. Oh, such treasures for her very own home, Mr. and Mrs. E.J. Miller's very own first home. She could not wait to get everything just right before E.J. came home.

That evening, as E.J. watched her bustle around, he decided he really was the luckiest man in this whole world. He felt that some of the ache in his heart was lifting. He was here to stay. No one, no one, would send him back now; this America and this Rosa Ellen, his precious little Liebchen, were his.

Rosa's little puppy was very mischievous and always chewing on everything. She said one day, "Oh, puppy dog, I have to have the patience of Job with you," and she laughed. "Well, Mama used to say that she needed the patience of Job with me too, so I guess your name is Job. Now Job, you stop that; no, you can't chew on that, no, no, Job."

After most of the stormy weather was over, Rosa was able to explore the home ranch a little. There was still some snow about, but she loved putting on her boots and wandering around. The ranch had thousands of acres, E.J. had told her. She walked around the main ranch house. It was big, a sprawling two-story house with a covered porch running around all four sides. There were two enormous barns that seemed to tower over everything else. There were several long bunkhouses and other sturdy looking sheds, a blacksmith shop, where Anthony, Mrs. Commery's husband, was totally in charge. There were all kinds of pens and holding yards for animals and a big, long root cellar with a rounded top. She figured it was covered with soil, although now it was just a long round hump of snow. Rosa thought of her own tiny root cellar on the Homestead and still got that proud feeling that she herself had dug it and laid the rock stairs and floor. She was happy to think that Henry and Blanche were making good use of "Rosa's root cellar."

But down in this ranch root cellar there was every kind of food you could imagine. Hanging in rows were huge slabs of meats and hams and sausages. There were big round cheeses on shelves, large crocks of saurkraut and pickles. There was every kind of root vegetable, dried fruits, and rows and rows of big gallon canning jars filled with lots of tasty looking things; they had glass lids and heavy clamps to hold the lid secure. There were even apples kept in a big crock and still pretty good, even this late in the winter. All of this food was raised right on the ranch. A huge vegetable garden was tended by the Mexicans, and a large fruit orchard marched all the way down to the small river that ran through the meadow. This was like a small town, right here. Rosa marveled again and again that any one man could own such a fine spread. Out beyond the barns were the help's cabins, all in a row, all surrounded by willow trees. Mrs. Commery told her, "There are real pretty wild trumpet vines and lots of wild roses and hollyhocks that will bloom this spring for you Missus, and they always look mighty purty."

Rosa couldn't have been happier. This ranch was a dream ranch, and she and E.J. were safe here, too. She wondered if originally, a long time ago, this had been just a small, poor homestead, just like Henry's.

Oh, she was so content—she had E.J., and she had her own cozy little cabin. There was Mrs. Commery, who was becoming a dear, dear friend. There were the three families of Mexican workers living on the ranch. Rosa made friends with the mothers and finally overcame the shyness of the children, some eight of them. They often would come and visit with her. She started to teach them some words in English, and they seemed eager to learn. Oh, she thought, I can be a teacher right here. I will talk to E.J. about starting my own school for these children. She was very excited about this plan.

In getting settled, she had forgotten the large parcel in her trunk that Cook and the maids at the household in Pocatello had given her. Then one rainy day she remembered and lay the parcel out on the table and cut the strings. Yes, there was a large bolt of light blue muslin with tiny pink flowers all over it. Oh, that will make a lovely spring gown, she thought. Underneath was another parcel, still wrapped, but in old, very browned paper. She looked at what was written on the package, faded but readable; why, it was addressed to Miss Harrietta Styvenson, at the address where Rosa had worked, the unhappy Aunt Harrietta, and pinned to the browned paper was a white note. She opened that and read:

Dear Rosa,

This package contains a wedding dress and six petticoats, all of the finest, softest linen from Ireland. Many, many years ago, Miss Harrietta had this made up and it was delivered to the house, but something terrible must have happened because she never got married. Some years ago, Harrietta told Cook to burn this package, but Cook could not do that, she just stashed it away. Then we all talked it over and we thought that you could use this nice soft linen for making baby clothes for your first born, so we hope you will accept this and maybe it will make up for the awful way that Harrietta always treated you.

Have a happy life Rosa, we send you our sincerest regards, from Cook, Marissa and Clarabelle.

Well, well, oh my goodness, she thought, I don't know what to make of this. Those ladies, they must have had a fine time planning this, and oh, how thoughtful of them. They must have known that I would never have taken this had I known what it really was. Oh, those ladies, they are such special friends, I must write them right away.

She quickly unwrapped the parcel, and the lovely white linen, all folded in tissue paper, fell across the table. It was soft and beautiful, and it took her breath away. When she held up the gown she could tell that it was a large size, large enough for a lady like Miss Harrietta. It was a simple wedding dress but with delicate lace insets and tucks all over the bodice and sleeves. There were rows of fine lace around the bottom and around each petticoat. Rosa sat with the beautiful dress draped over her lap, and tears of regret flowed down. "Oh, poor Miss Harrietta, what could have happened to her intended marriage? How sad, how very sad, no wonder she was so unhappy. Whatever happened must have turned her into that bitter lady. Oh, I'm so sorry, Miss Harrietta, so very sorry."

E.J. came in and saw her there with the tears streaming down. "Rosa, Liebchen, what is it?" She told him, showing him the beautiful things, and he kissed away her tears. "Well, Mrs. Miller, surely someting good vill come from dis because you vill have da best gowned baby in dis whole country, und Miss Harrietta Styvenson vould surely be proud."

Spring was slow coming to the Utah valley, but Rosa was out on her bay mare almost every day, exploring and watching the hands at work. Little Job-dog was always bounding happily along at her horse's heels. Although she was not riding her Kit, she loved to be riding again, to be out in the wide open spaces, to feel the wind, to see the hawks soaring, and yes, there were some of those pesky jack-rabbits here, too. She always smiled when she saw them, "You critters are safe from me here, I hope you know that."

When she knew E.J. was working anywhere near, she would ride out with his noonday meal, and they would sit in a sheltered place and enjoy the sun. Greenery was sprouting everywhere, and away in the distance, the beauty of the blue mountains surrounded the valley. How could anyone be any happier than Mrs. E.J. Miller? Rosa often mused to herself. Here she was, a grown up married lady, married to her handsome cowboy and a long way from poor little "Skinny Scotty, the Rebel Brat."

She was anxious to help with the gardens, and whenever any of the men were working there, she was quick to help. The Mexican workers smiled at her. They could not imagine the boss' Missus wanting to get her little hands dirty.

Each day was a dream come true, and she looked forward eagerly to the time when she and E.J could lie together, holding each other, talking over the day, thinking of the future, "but not always just talkin'," she would say with a giggle.

There was just that one fear that would grasp Rosa whenever someone rode up to the ranch. Sometimes a wagon of another rancher would come in, and that made her uneasy until they knew who it was. Oftentimes she had visions of a man, perhaps a German military man, coming and taking her E.J. away. But she should not think about that; they were safe out here, and surely, if anyone was in the area looking for E.J., Sheriff Pete would know about it.

In late spring, Sheriff Pete did come riding out. He came along with a ranch-hand bringing in the spring supplies from Tremonton. Pete told E.J. that everything was alright, and Rosa breathed a sigh of relief.

There was a very rowdy supper that evening. Sheriff Pete was a favorite with all the men. Mrs. Commery had prepared a huge meal with lots of special pies. Pete told her, "I always eat enough for three men when I come out here, Mrs. Commery. You are the best dern cook in this here whole state." And at that, she bustled around and cut him another slab of sweet potato pie.

Sheriff Pete, as promised, brought Rosa and E.J.'s "weddin' pitchers." They were even framed in an ornate gold-filigreed twin frame. Rosa was, of course, delighted with this gift.

The next morning E.J. and Rosa saddled up and rode a ways with Pete. He was on his way south, down the valley to visit a couple more ranches. They stopped on the brow of a knoll and stepped down to say good-by. "Well, E.J.," Pete told them, "there is war now all over Europe. It's terrible, and maybe this United States will keep out of it, but nobody knows. I think you are pretty safe from the Germans now, but my advice is that you just stay out here. Anyway, you big galoot, you look like one happy fella, and Missus, you are blooming. This ranch life must be jest your cup-a-tea. Well, so long you two, and I am sure pleased to visit with you all again."

Rosa was beside herself with joy at the supplies that were brought in for her. There was a large package from the mercantile in Tremonton that held her order. She had ordered some nice heavy twill so that she could make herself up a divided riding skirt. She remembered seeing one in a shop window in Pocatello and was determined to have one. Oh, how she wished she could just wear britches like the men—it wasn't fair at all. Also she had ordered some boots for riding. They were very sturdy and laced up with leather thongs. She would certainly be comfy in those. She could not wait to get to her stitching and make up the riding skirt, and she wanted to make up some serviceable shirtwaists. She had enough material to make up two of those.

Arriving with the supplies was the ever welcome mail. The ranch received mail only about four times a year, so it was a very special time. Rosa had a pack of letters, two from her Mama, others from her sisters and Henry, one from Uncle Albert in Nebraska, and even two from her sisters back in Indiana. Oh, there was a letter from Marissa in Pocatello and one from the minister's wife, Dulcie. And there was even a big package of newspapers from Miss Stanton in Springfield who was still schoolmarm there—my what excitement! She opened one or two letters each evening and read them aloud to E.J. This took many evenings, and then there were the newspapers to read from cover to cover. There were many articles about the terrible war that Germany was waging on its neighbors in Europe. E.J. was always quiet for a long time after she finished reading these. This news made him very sad, indeed.

Her mama's letter did not mention her health, but sister Louisa voiced her concern at Mama's failing a little each day. It was a degenerating kidney problem, the doctor had told them, and he was doing all he could for her. Henry's letter told of his farming successes and his failures with the crops, and best of all, news of her Kit horse, who, he said, was growing fatter and sassier all the time.

In early fall of that year, Mr. H.K. Wilie, the ranch owner, was expected. He had sent word that he would be bringing four or five men with him for the fall hunting. The whole ranch was soon humming with a major cleanup project. E.J. was out giving all kinds of orders to make the ranch shine. They had to make sure the boss's tack was all ready and the horses newly shod for the guests. Fresh whitewash was needed on all the fences and corrals. The barns must be gone through and properly spruced up. Fortunately, Mr. E.J. was a stickler for immediate repairs— a broken fence rail, a gate, or anything that needed attention, was fixed up as soon as it was noticed, so this special sprucing up was not too difficult. The Mexican ladies had to completely air out the guest rooms and freshen up the ranch house. Mrs. Commery was busier than anyone else. She was bustling in her kitchen, checking supplies from dawn to dark, getting everything prepared for the boss and the "city gentlemen."

Mr. Wilie and four men arrived in a big double buggy, with the boot piled high. They had large leather bags and big rifles in leather carrying cases. Rosa watched their arrival from her doorway, and she couldn't help but smile at all the loud, good natured talk. They seemed in wonderful spirits. Well, why not, their trip had been made in a comfy buggy and in lovely warm weather. They would have seen all the fall colors ablaze. It must have been a wonderful trip for them.

Mr. Wilie and his guests had their meals in the main dining room of the ranch house with Luca doing the serving. That first night, Mrs. Commery put out a special meal for everyone, as she always did when the big boss was home. After supper, E.J. told Rosa that Mr. Wilie would like to meet her, so they walked over to the main house and into the study. Mr. Wilie was short and stout, and he was smoking a big cigar. He was not as old as she had imagined but had thinning brown hair. He had a round face and a kind of impish grin. He took both of her hands and looked her up and down with eyes that were small and round. "Well, well, E.J., look at this little filly. She sure is a pretty thing. How did a big Kraut like you snag such a dainty lady? My hearty congratulations to you, Mrs. Miller. I hope I'm not too late to kiss the blushing bride."

He leaned over and planted a rather moist kiss on her cheek. She stepped back and curtsied as formally as she could. "Thank you very much, Mr. Wilie; it is a pleasure to meet you."

Mr. Wilie reached up and clapped E.J. on the shoulder. "You ol' son of a gun, you didn't tell me she was such a looker. You really found yourself a pretty little filly. I thought you were crazy to run off to Idaho in winter to look for your gal, but she sure was worth lookin for, and how do you like livin' out here, Mrs. Miller?" he asked, still looking her over.

Rosa was quick to tell him, "Oh, Mr. Wilie, this ranch is a beautiful place, and I like living here very much."

He asked her to sit and offered E.J. a cigar, and they talked for awhile about ranch business, how the pastures were holding up, the alfalfa crop, moving the stock, and so on. As they were leaving, Mr. Wilie again took both her hands and squeezed them.

The next day, Rosa could not stop thinking about Mr. Wilie. Of course he was a very powerful man, and they said that someday he might even be a Senator. Imagine that, a Senator! She could tell that he was very aware of his wealth and power, but, but well, she just did not like him, not at all. She kept rubbing her cheek; he had made her feel like part of the livestock—filly, indeed!

But wait, this man had been very good to E.J. He had had enough confidence in a young German immigrant to make him foreman of this huge ranch. E.J. was in charge, and that was a tremendous responsibility when an owner was seldom around. But then, perhaps also, Mr. Wilie knew that E.J. was an illegal in this country. Oh yes, and perhaps Mr. Wilie liked the fact that E.J. never left the ranch, was always right here, except those two weeks when he had come looking for her. So, for those years before she came, E.J. had never ever left this ranch. He was always here, and he worked so diligently and was intelligent in all his decisions for the ranch. Of course, Mr. Wilie would be good to E.J.; he was a very valuable man.

Oh dear, she should not think these things. Maybe she was jumping to the wrong conclusions. He was probably just one of those men who were affectionate and patted and touched everyone. She wondered what Mrs. Wilie was like. Mrs. Commery had told her that Mrs. Wilie had never come way out here to this ranch in Utah. She lived in Boise, Idaho, and only seldom even visited the Wilie ranch in Springfield, Idaho.

The ranch bustled the next few weeks with Mr. Wilie and his guests going out hunting almost every day. They brought in many deer, several wolves, and even a large mountain lion. Rosa saw it hanging over the pack mule's back and recognized it from pictures she had seen of the lions that lived in the mountains, sometimes called a puma.

One day, as Rosa was returning to the ranch after taking E.J. his noon meal, she met up with Mr. Wilie and two of his guests coming in from their morning hunt. She was on her horse with Job trotting beside her. "Well, Mrs. Miller, good afternoon," Mr. Wilie called to her as they all pulled their horses to a stop. "My, you sit a fine seat, you surely do. Oh boys, this is Mrs. Miller, E.J.'s private little filly," and the men touched their hats. Then the three men just sat there looking her over as she calmly controlled the prancing mare. She felt their eyes on her slouch hat held down with the light scarf over it and tied under her chin, with her long braid hanging down her back. Anyway, she knew she was tidy in her neat shirtwaist, the slim fitting jacket and long split riding skirt. She sat straight in the saddle and tried to smile. "How do you do, gentlemen," she said clearly. They tipped their hats again at her as Mr. Wilie said, "Well, boys, let's get on to the ranch, I feel the need of a whiskey," and they moved off, pulling the loaded pack mule. But Rosa could still feel eyes on her.

She rode back slowly. She had felt very uncomfortable at that meeting. Maybe rich men, powerful rich men, were just different. Well, she would be glad to see them go.

Their first Christmas at the ranch was quiet. E.J. had brought in a real pine tree, a small one he had cut way up on the mountain. Rosa strung it with popcorn and made pretty bows out of scraps of any colored cloth she could find. She remembered a wild holly tree she had seen, so she took out the mare and brought back a whole sackfull of boughs with red berries to brighten up the cabin.

Everyone had Christmas dinner in the big ranch kitchen; all the hands and all the Mexican families crowded around the long table. There were carols and rowdy talk, and everyone had a wonderful time. Then E.J and Rosa spent a lovely quiet evening in their decorated cabin, drinking hot cider, sitting close together, and talking about their one year of being married. Oh, how she loved her E.J., and she loved being here with him. What a special, special Christmas time!

The winter was again severe, but Rosa did not mind, and she knew by February that she was probably with child. E.J. was beside himself. "Are you sure, Rosa, are you sure?" he kept asking over and over. "Und Liebchen, you must be veddy, veddy careful now."

Mrs. Commery was very helpful in telling Rosa what to expect because Rosa really did not know one thing about having a baby. After the first few months she felt wonderful and continued to ride and help out in the gardens and help with the cooking chores when needed. She just bloomed and went around humming all the time. She quickly made up two nice hubbard gowns to wear.

Then that summer, when she was about six months along, and already fairly large, a frightening thing happened. Whenever she went down into the big root-cellar to get some supplies for Mrs. Commery, she always put her hand up on the rock ledge to steady herself as she made her way down the steep steps to the door of the cellar. That morning she laid her hand on something large and almost warm and very, very silky, and it moved. She instantly was frozen with fear; she jerked her hand away. She looked closely, and she could just make out a monstrous dark snake beginning to uncurl. It was looking at her, and the forked tongue was flicking in and out right at eye level with her. She screamed, dropped her basket, and ran out into the sunlight crying out at the top of her voice. A Mexican worker ran to her and tried to calm her, but he could not understand what was the matter. Finally, Mrs. Commery came running to her out of the house. When she realized what Rosa was saying, she helped her over to the porch, calming her, saying, "Oh, my goodness, Missus, that is just ol' Ebenezer, our bull snake. He has been on the ranch forever. He won't hurt you; we like him here 'cause he eats rats and varmints, and sometimes when it is very warm, he likes to sleep there in the stairwell of the cellar. Oh Missus, he won't hurt you. He is a nice ol' snake, but I can see he would be scary for a lady who did not know 'bout him. Now, just set here a spell, and I will bring you some tea. Shush now, shush. It's alright."

Rosa was shaken. What a terrible fright that was! A snake, a huge monster of a snake. She did not know they ever got that large. She could still feel the warm, satiny softness of his coil under her hand, and she shuddered again. She was not afraid of snakes; she had had many garden snakes as pets when she was a child, but maybe this one gave her such a fright because he was so huge. But wait, yes, she had heard somewhere that if a woman with child was frightened by a snake, that her unborn would be marked in some way. Oh no, that could not be so, that must be one of those "old wives' tales" she had heard all her life. There was nothing to that, it could not be true. But, from then on, a small fear was always lurking deep inside. "Oh please, Lord, make my baby healthy and perfect. Please, Lord," she prayed every single night.

Her thoughtful husband had made plans to take her into Tremonton, and then she was to take the train on to Mama and Belle's home in Burley, and she was to go a good month before the baby was due. Rosa actually argued with him about this for many evenings, but he would not hear of her having their child way out on this ranch, far from a doctor and the help she would need from her mama and sisters. Yes, Rosa was happy to think about seeing Mama and realized that he was being sensible, but she did not want to leave. She didn't want to. But E.J. would not hear of her staying, and that was that, so she finally had to agree to go.

That first of August 1916, E.J. drove her to Tremonton in the ranch buggy. Even though she was large and uncomfortable, the trip was not too bad. They stopped often so she could walk and rest. At the half-way stop over at the Culpepper's ranch, they had a wonderful visit, and Rosa received a lot more good advice about birthin' and babies from kind Mrs. Culpepper, who had birthed seven of her own.

When they reached Tremonton, they had another nice supper with Sheriff Pete. He was full of news, especially about the war in Europe. He told them how the politicians all over the country were fighting over whether or not the United States should enter into the war.

Early the next morning E.J. put her on the train. It was very difficult to say good-by, as she was crying the whole time. Oh, she did not want to do this; only the thought of seeing her mama again made it possible for her to leave him. She was tired and uncomfortable during the long rattley train ride to Burley and arrived very, very weary.

There was Harry waiting again, Louisa's nice husband, and soon she was happily greeted at Belle's home. But, oh, her heart was heavy when she saw how frail her mama looked. But now she was so glad, so thankful, that Mr. Miller had insisted she come. Her mama was beaming with joy at having Rosa come stay with them, and it all seemed worthwhile just seeing her mama's face.

During the next weeks the ladies were busy stitching lovely baby clothes, as Rosa had brought along the beautiful linen wedding dress and petticoats. Her mama and her sisters kept asking her again and again to tell them the story of poor Miss Harrietta.

Her time came, and Rosa finally knew that strange, unearthly pain of birth. Mama told her it would be difficult, but how could anyone tell you about that? As Rosa was a small girl, the painful birthing was long and tedious and exhausting. The only thing that helped was some of Louisa's special tea; it seemed to take the edge off the excruciating pain. Finally, a beautiful daughter was born; Dorothea Olive was born in early September of 1916. Rosa and E.J. had talked over possible names. If it were to be a boy, his name would be Pete Darrell Miller, and if a girl, then Dorothea for Rosa's great-grandmother with the middle name of Olive, which was E.J.'s grandmother's name.

Rosa's baby was chubby and healthy, a bright-eyed little girl. Rosa was so thankful to the Lord that her baby was complete and healthy—and without a single odd mark on her fat little body. Mama was beside herself with joy, and Rosa was so thankful that she was with her family and learning so much from her sisters and Mama, for there was much she did not know about caring for a newborn.

Sister Louisa had had another baby too, a girl, and she told Rosa that she would have no problems. Being a mother was easy, it would all just come naturally, she would see. Mama loved to sit in her rocker and hold the baby for hours, and Rosa knew she would always remember her sitting there rocking the little thing and singing so softly.

Three weeks after Dorothea was born, Rosa was ready to go back to the ranch. Oh, she missed her E.J. so much and could not wait for him to see his new little daughter.

Rosa knew that when she said good-by to Mama this time, it was probably a final good-by. The doctor had told Rosa the sad truth—her mama would not be here very much longer.

"Now little Rosey," Mama told her, "you have made me so happy, just coming here for the birthing, and I want you to tell Mr. Miller how thankful I am that he decided you should come. Now little Rosey, my little Rose-bud, don't you cry. Don't be sad for me, Rosey. I will soon be with my angels and it will be beautiful, I know. But I want you to remember, Rosey, that I will always be with you. I will always be watching over you, my little Rose-bud. Don't ever forget that. I will always be with you."

The long train ride back to Tremonton was tiresome, but she was so anxious that the time went quickly, and the baby was quiet and content. A telegraph message had been sent to Sheriff Pete about when to expect her, and sure enough, there was E.J. himself waiting at the station when she stepped down with the baby in her arms. E.J. hugged both of them in one of his big bear hugs. Then he watched in fascination as she pulled the soft blanket back so he could look at his daughter. He tenderly caressed the baby's face with one finger and huge tears formed in his eyes. He couldn't speak, he just looked into Rosa's face.

After a day in Tremonton, they returned to the ranch. It was a glorious fall with every bush and tree gold in the sun. Rosa was filled with joy about everything.

They arrived at the ranch just a few days before Mr. Wilie and guests were expected for the fall hunting season again. Rosa pitched in and helped out; Mrs. Commery and Luca had endless kitchen details, as Mrs. Commery not only had the usual hands to cook for, but also Mr. Wilie's guests. These guests seemed to be very, very important men, so careful preparations were made for special dishes to be served. Rosa was glad she did not have to talk with Mr. Wilie or any of his guests, although they all raised their hats politely in passing.

Her baby girl was a happy baby. She had dark hair, lots of it, and her eyes looked like they were starting to turn from blue to her daddy's hazel color. Soon her hair took on an almost auburn color, and it was curly. She was an exceptionally pretty little girl, and Mrs. Commery, Luca, all the hands, and all the Mexican children wanted to look at her and coo at her.

Rosa had plenty of milk, and nursing her baby in her quiet cabin was a time of great pleasure for her. At these times she always thought of her dear mama, and tears would flow. Mama had passed away just three weeks after Rosa had said good-by to her. Rosa's thoughts of her mama would always remind her of a poem that she had read someplace. Somehow, when she repeated it aloud to her baby girl, her heartache would ease a little:

Tho I have had to leave you, whom I love,
To go along the silent way,
Grieve not, nor speak of me with tears,
But laugh and talk of me as if I were beside you,
For who knows that I shall be, oft times.

So, when you hear a word I used to say,
Or touch a thing I loved,
Let not your heart be sad, for I am happy here with Jesus,
And I am loving you,
Just as I always have.

Oh, how Rosa missed her sweet mama; but she felt that Mama was happy now. And she knew that Mama would always be looking over her. Mama would always be there.

That winter the days passed quickly. The weather was not as severe as the last two winters had been, and Rosa was thankful for that.

Very early on a February morning, Luca came pounding on their cabin door frantically calling out, "Rosah, Missus, come quick, Mrs. Commery, someting wrong. Mrs. Commery awful sick!" E.J. and Rosa rushed quickly to the Commery cabin. Her husband Anthony was there waiting and hurried them inside to the bed. Mrs. Commery was writhing back and forth in agony. "She have some kind of attack, I tink," Anthony told them. "Missus, what we do? What we do?"

Rosa laid cool cloths on Mrs. Commery's stomach where the pain was and sent E.J. to the ranch house for some laudanum which she knew was kept there for emergencies. She sent Luca's daughter, Teresa, back to Rosa's cabin to care for the baby and had Luca bring her some herbs and brew up some tea which might help calm the pain. When E.J. brought the laudanum, Rosa told him, "She has had other attacks, but nothing like this. Not this severe, and they never lasted this long. Oh E.J., there is nothing we can do for her—she needs a doctor, and soon."

They all decided they must get her to town as soon as they could. It would take a rider a full four days, maybe more, to return with a doctor. Taking her that long way might be too much for her, but they must do something. There was no other way; they could not just let her lie here and suffer and not try to do something. Fortunately, there was enough laudanum, which appeared to be a great help with the pain, to get her through the long ride to a doctor.

They decided that Luca would go along with Mrs. Commery's husband, Anthony, who would be driving the wagon. Rosa made sure that there were two feather mattresses put in the wagon with lots of comforters and warmed bricks for her feet. Luca was given careful instructions about giving Mrs. Commery the laudanum doses every few hours. The best horses were hitched up quickly. Mrs. Commery was groggy but grasped Rosa's hand. "Now Rosa," she said, "you stay and look after things, and make sure my boys are fed. Rosa, will you do that please, till I get back?"

The following days dragged by. They had no way of knowing what was happening, and Rosa was so afraid for Mrs. Commery. Then in one week, Mr. Commery and Luca came driving up the lane. Mrs. Commery had died while the doctor was trying to do an operation called an appendectomy. Everyone was shocked and saddened. Oh, nothing would ever be the same without Mrs. Commery.

Rosa had kept her promise to feed Mrs. Commery's boys, but the food she prepared was not very good—actually, it was terrible. Rosa had never really learned to cook very well. Her sisters, especially Louisa, always did the cooking when Rosa was young. Rosa had just run away from the cooking and canning at the Homestead, and here at the ranch, helping with the peeling and stirring and such had not taught her how to plan and prepare huge meals for ten or twelve hungry hands. Oh, she had prepared the few simple meals for herself and E.J., but fixing a simple stew for two was not the same as cooking three full meals a day. Mrs. Commery had even sent over all the breads and biscuits that Rosa and E.J. needed because Rosa's cook-stove would not bake anything; it just burned everything they tried in it.

So now, Rosa was faced with a great challenge. She was the only one to do this. Even Luca was not too much help. Oh, she did make up a mean pot of beans and made wonderful tortillas, but the men were used to more than that kind of meal every day.

Well, it was a challenge, and Rosa, with her usual bravado, would just pitch in and put out one edible meal, then two very bad ones. Her biscuits and breads were the real problem. There were no cookbooks, no recipe cards, none. Even though they searched through the library in the main ranch house, no cookbook could be found.

Rosa experimented, tried everything she could think of with the biscuits and breads, trying to remember just what Louisa and Mrs. Commery had put in them—a pinch of this, a handful of that, no, next time more flour, no, less butter, oh dear. She was beside herself. Her bread would fall and become too soggy to even cut. And the biscuits— well they were never right.

Rosa felt as if her whole world had fallen in on top of her—Mama passing and now Mrs. Commery, too. Poor Mrs. Commery, she mourned, she was such a dear, dear friend. Oh, how I miss you, Missus. I wish you would just come bustling back into this kitchen and tease me and tell me why my bread won't rise and my biscuits are so hard.

Fortunately, the hands and E.J. realized she was trying very hard. They all tried to be good natured about it all. One morning she set the big, round platter of biscuits on the table, and they looked pretty good, so all the hands grabbed them up. The first man that took a bite hollered out, "Look out, this here biscuit is hard as nails. It'll sure chip yer tooth if yer not careful." Another started tapping his biscuit on the table, then another and then another. At that moment, E.J. came in through the kitchen door. "Hey boss," one of them called, "catch this," and he threw a biscuit at E.J. E.J. laughingly threw it back and hit the cowhand, and everyone guffawed. "Now, these here would make good bombs," one fellow shouted, and biscuits started flying all over the kitchen. Rosa knew they were having fun and letting off steam, but she felt so bad and just darn exasperated about it all. Well, what could she do? She just started throwing biscuits too, and landed one right on the back of E.J.'s head. The men roared for ten minutes at that.

Later E.J. apologized for the men and for his part in the teasing and held her while she sobbed and told him that she really did not know what to do. She had tried everything.

The next day, E.J. was gone till dark, and when he finally came in, he had a whiskered dirty old man in tow, riding a mule. "Well, Mrs. Miller," E.J. told her, "here da present for you. Dis here is Jonah. He, vel da sort of cook, he vonce cooked on da chuckwagon. Jonah, dis pretty lady is my wife, und if you don't teach her how to make da good biscuits, I vill tan your hide mit my bull-whip."

But before Rosa would let this "gift" even near her kitchen, she made E.J. take him out to the wash-house to get rid of that strange odor. Then she started getting lessons in just what should go into biscuits and breads and such. She quickly learned the secrets of biscuit making. She had put the wrong amount of replenishing ingredients into her sourdough starter. That was the main problem, and so on and so on. In a short time the meals improved, and she even put out some passable pies.

Jonah was a grizzled old fellow with very dark skin. He said his mama was a full-blooded Shoshone Indian, and Rosa did not doubt this story for a minute. He was kind, and he dearly loved to lean over and make odd grunting noises with little Dorothea lying in her basket in the corner of the kitchen.

So, life settled down, and they waited for the new cook to arrive any day now, but somehow, one never came. It seemed it was Rosa's misfortune to be the only woman there to feed the hands something besides beans every day. Well, she thought to herself, a lot of women would love to do all this cooking. Louisa would just love this, with the endless supply of food to choose from. Mrs. Commery really liked to do it too, but somehow I have a terrible dislike of cooking. I hate to be cooped up here in this steamy kitchen. I never have liked to be anywhere near one of these darn ol' big iron cook-stoves.

She did the best she could. She must tend to little Dorothea, plan and cook three large meals a day for twelve men, and that meant doing all the baking, making bread every single day, and rolls and those biscuits, too. Fortunately, she had Luca and one of the other Mexican ladies to help with all the odd chores and to clean up, so that was a great help. Luca's oldest daughter, Teresa, who was about eleven years old, was very good at taking care of the baby; so, after nursing Dorothea, Rosa had to let Teresa look after her.

That summer, Mr. Wilie came to the ranch for a couple of weeks. He was alone this time, said he wanted to catch up on the workings of the ranch, and he told E.J. that he wanted to plan on cultivating many more acres in the valley for growing more alfalfa. They discussed how he was going to grow a special alfalfa, just for making seed to sell. He would be able to sell seed and make a much greater profit than he would just growing it to feed his cattle all winter. E.J. was to hire more men, and there would even be a tractor and other equipment sent out soon. The special irrigation must be planned, and of course, much more fencing would be needed. His plan, he told E.J., was to eventually cut down his herds and get more and more into just growing alfalfa seed to ship all over the West. Oh, he had great plans.

When E.J. related all these new plans to Rosa, he seemed very unhappy. When she asked him about this, he said that he was not a farmer, he did not know about farming. He did not like to be a farmer, and he hated to see the cattle herds go, because that meant that the horse herds would no longer be necessary either.

Rosa was relieved that Mr. Wilie just came in and sat down and ate with the men. He was polite to her and very preoccupied most of the time. E.J. had approached Mr. Wilie again about seriously finding a permanent cook like he had said he would, and Mr. Wilie told him he was sorry, that he certainly would find one as soon as he got back to town.

Mr. Wilie would come into the kitchen once in a while during the day and request a cup of tea from Rosa, and they would chat a few minutes. He always managed to put his hand on her shoulder or brush against her when she refilled his cup. But he seemed pleasant enough, and Rosa tried to overlook her first opinion of him.

One day Rosa was making her usual trip down into the root cellar for her supplies when she realized that Mr. Wilie was coming down the narrow staircase. They spoke a little about the supplies in the cellar. Rosa continued to fill her basket and was lifting a tied bundle of turnips when he actually came up behind her, put one arm around her waist and with the other brushed his hand up and cupped her breast with his fat hand.

She recoiled with disgust, immediately swung around with the bundle of turnips in her hand, and hit him square in the face with the turnip tops. She heard a swishing noise but realized that she had not hurt him. Well, she didn't care. The nerve! She wished she had hit him with the turnips instead of just the tops.

She heard his laugh as she dropped her basket and headed for the doorway. "My, my, Rosa, you are a feisty little filly, you surely are. Why, I was just havin' a little fun with you, wanted to see if those were real. They sure are plumped out real nice." But she didn't hear any more as she hurried out and across the yard to her cabin.

Oh no, oh no, how could this happen? Why did some men have to be so offensive? She was red and flushed and extremely angry. She knew she had never liked Mr. Wilie, but now she hated him. This big important man, going to be a Senator, grabbing at her like that. Oh, she could forgive that young man in Pocatello. He was just a spoiled child, but Mr. Wilie was supposed to be a "gentleman." Oh dear, what should she do? Oh no, oh no, she could never tell Mr. Miller. With his explosive German temperament, he would just beat the man senseless or maybe even kill him, and then E.J. would be in serious trouble. No, she would never let her Mr. Miller know about this. E.J. respected Mr. Wilie as a good boss. She mulled this over in her mind again and again and decided, I will just have to forget this, just never be alone when Mr. Wilie is anywhere around; maybe it won't happen again. He surely took a wollop with those old, dried up turnip tops, and she smiled a little. I wish I'd had a big ham in my hand instead. But she was shaken, and in the next days and weeks, a strange kind of feeling came over her. This was not really their home at all, this was Mr. Wilie's ranch and everything and everyone here belonged to him. Well, *she* sure didn't, no siree, *she* didn't.

Mr. Wilie came to the ranch two more times that year, and in September he again brought out six hunting friends. But he also brought a young man to act as his private cook. At least Rosa was spared from having to cook for another seven men and to see that they were served properly. The young man was agreeable and helpful, and he and Rosa worked well together. He taught her many interesting ways to cook, and he laughed when she told him how much she could have used his help when the hard tack biscuits were flying all over her kitchen like so many bullets.

Mr. Wilie had told E.J. that he was having trouble finding a cook to come way out here, but that he would increase Rosa's wage and give her a bonus, too. E.J. was not happy about this and told Mr. Wilie that he did not want his wife to work as the cook. He wanted Mr. Wilie to keep looking for a replacement.

Well, Rosa was very pleased by the extra money, but she was not happy. The fall canning was in full progress, and even with the several helpers, she worked from dawn till way after dark. She felt she was neglecting her baby. Even though Dorothea was in the kitchen a lot, always being looked after by Teresa, Rosa still did not have any time to be with the baby, and this really bothered her.

Things never stay the same, she often thought to herself. I do so miss the easy friendship of Mrs. Commery. I miss not being able to play with my own baby, and I really miss not being able to ride over the land or work out in the gardens. Oh, how I would love to be outdoors on these beautiful fall days! In order to keep teaching the young Mexican children, she insisted that each day the boys and girls come into the kitchen, sit at the long table and recite the simple lessons she gave them, while she and their mothers worked.

The quiet time she spent nursing her baby was the joy of her busy life. Such a tiny, helpless life, a precious life that was part Rosa and part big E.J. She would sit in her rocking chair in the cabin, and that was always a time of reflection, of prayer. She missed her mama, she missed Mrs. Commery, and oh how she missed her Kit-horse! Just to be out riding, feeling the soft breeze on her face, would be heaven. But that was not to be, and now she felt her life was not her own. It belonged to the Wilie Ranch.

In the evenings she always felt proud when Mr. Miller came rushing in and made such a fuss over his little daughter. He was one proud father. He held her and bounced her and marveled at her every move and gurgle.

In the early spring of 1918, Rosa was still doing the cooking, and five more men had been added to E.J.'s crew. The big tractor had arrived by freight wagon, and there were great plans to put many more hundreds of acres of land under cultivation.

One day, Sheriff Pete came riding out and hurried down to the south fields to look for E.J. Rosa heard one of the Mexicans telling Pete where E.J. was working that day, but Pete was gone before she got out the kitchen door. Oh no, oh no! She grasped the porch rail and hung on; now the worst had happened, and this could only mean danger for E.J.

In about an hour, the two men came riding hard into the yard. Hearing the horses, she ran out and down the steps. They stepped down, and E.J. put his arm around her. "My cousin, Hans, is in Tremonton, Leibchen. I must go und talk mit him—no it is not dat Kreuger, it is my own cousin. Pete tot it better dat I go to town, speak mit him dere. Hans said he knew dat I vas here on da Wilie ranch, so dat's all dat I can do, just go und talk mit him. You know dat I vill not go back. Maybe I can explain to Hans. I always liked cousin Hans. He is older but vas alvays goot to me as boy. Tank goodness dey send him und not vone of my broders; dey are all too much like Papa. Now, now, don't be afraid like dat; all dese years, I have expect dis. I vill ride in und speak mit him. Und listen, Pete says dat he found out dat now ve are married und ve have child, dat I am not too much illegal any more mit America, und mit da var going on, maybe Germans cannot force me to go back. I must go, Rosa. You see dat I have to do dis; now stop dat, don't cry, Liebchen, I be back soon, I promise, I be back."

Then E.J. and Pete rode off at a swift pace. Now her world really crumpled around her. She could not feel anything except the horror that he was gone. She almost ran out and saddled up the mare to gallop after them. She got as far as the barn when Teresa called after her, "Missus, Missus, the babe cries. It her feeding time. She hungry, Missus. Missus, where are you? So Rosa went back and sat in her rocking chair nursing her baby, feeling completely helpless. What would happen to him? Maybe they would put him in handcuffs and take him away—maybe she would never see him again?

Days went dragging by. All the help joined ranks to give her as much support as they could. Evidently they knew what the problem was by now and how terrified she was. Probably she was in shock, and maybe that helped, but those next four days were a living hell. On the fourth night he came riding hard into the ranch yard. It was very late, but she heard the pounding hooves and ran to her door. He came running and held her and said, "It's alright now, Liebchen, it's alright now."

Later, lying with her in his arms, he told her of the meeting with Hans. "You vould not believe, Rosa, Hans had already decide he vould not force me to go back even if he could. Und you know, Hans himself has decided to stay in America. Yes, it true, he has been here over a year now. Da others have look for me but den dey sent him. He had orders to locate me und ten odders und make us go back to Germany. He had message from Papa for me, und I best not tell you vat he say. Papa is fanatic about his sons to be officers in Wilhelm's army. He said dey should shoot me on sight if I not return. But poor Hans vould not harm anyone. I felt sorry for him; he had already persuaded four boys to go back, und den he decide he could not do dat anymore, dat he himself did not vant to go back. Oh Rosa, dis land, dis America, somehow, somevay it gets into da heart, and soon you vould never go back to tyranny of da Germany. Do you know dat Hans is going to San Francisco in California and start new life dere? Yes, dat's vhat he told me, und he said he has found all but one of da boys on his list und also told dem dis. He talked long time about terrible fighting in Europe. He say da Kaiser is mad mit power, und he fears for our people. Dis United States is sending many more fighting men over dere, und many vil be dying. It is veddy terrible, terrible to tink about."

Rosa was still frightened for E.J.'s safety, and a few days later she asked him if Hans had said anything about that awful Kreuger man. E.J. just shrugged and said quickly, "I guess dat dey must have request him to return to da Homeland. Hans did not know anyting about him."

Rosa was puzzled by his answer and the look in his eyes when she had asked about Kreuger, so she did not ask any more questions. She later said that in all the years of their marriage, E.J. had never ever mentioned the Kreuger man again.

CHAPTER TWELVE

Lion of the Mountain, 1918

THE WORK ON THE RANCH CONTINUED. It seemed that spring and summer were long in coming this year. Rosa worked from dawn till dark every single day and tried to give her baby a little extra time. Little Dorothea was just big enough to want to walk now and was a handful for Teresa to keep up with, but Teresa was wonderful with her.

Rosa still missed Mrs. Commery so very much. She had no other women to talk with. The Mexican ladies only spoke a few words of English and did not seem to care to learn much more. But they did want their children to learn, so they made sure they were present when Rosa had the time to give them a few lessons. It was a very lonely time, and Rosa often thought how wonderful it would be to be able to go to church or to a quilting get-together with other ladies, just to talk. Oh, a social and a dance would be so nice! She wondered if she would ever get to dance with her handsome husband. If it were not for E.J.'s kind support and her beautiful baby girl, she would just about scream out every day with the frustration of being tied down in the ranch kitchen and the terrible loneliness she was feeling.

The days passed quickly, with Rosa up well before dawn. She had no time for herself, but once in a great while she would take a few minutes and go up on the hillside behind the ranch and look for roots and herbs. She had been slowly teaching herself about the local herbs the Mexican ladies used for different ailments. Oh, they looked just like weeds and funny twisted roots, but they were used for making tea, and although it tasted terrible, it seemed to be a good tonic for many things. She had been writing to Louisa about these tonics and enjoyed hearing from her wise sister about the different plants to use for seasonings and various teas.

One early summer day there was a breeze, so she slipped on a sweater, and leaving Teresa to watch over the napping baby, walked up on the hill with her little sack and digging tool. Her Job-dog bounded happily around her. Oh, he dearly loved to take a walk! My, the air smelled so fresh; it was heavy with the scent of sage in bloom. It was so peaceful. She stood for a while watching the blue and purple mountains around her, enjoying the solitude of the peaceful valley.

She had been digging some roots, moving slowly around one area, when she heard Job bark loudly and then growl and run back and forth behind her.

She started to rise up to look around when suddenly a huge blurred body came hurtling at her. Job snarled menacingly and launched his small body directly at the mountain lion leaping straight down on Rosa. A tumbling battle erupted instantly between the little dog and the lion. Rosa was pushed out of the way by the swirling bodies. The lion made ferocious snarling noises and a cloud of dust rose all around. She heard herself screaming, "No, no, get away, get away!" and she swung the small digging pick in her hand at the lion. She felt she landed one blow but could not be sure. She did not want to hit the dog. Oh, my God, my God, make it go away! No, no this can't be. Job! Job!

It all lasted only a few moments, but it seemed forever that she was trying to strike the lion. Then all of a sudden the cat bounded away back up the hill, still snarling menacingly, and there was Job, lying in a bloody heap in the dust. Oh no, oh no! She knelt over him. "Job, my little doggy, oh Job, are you hurt bad?" She quickly took off her sweater, wrapped the small dog up in it and carried him. Stumbling down the hill, she cried out at the top of her voice, "Come quick, help, Job is hurt, come quick!" One of the workers ran to her, took the small bundle from her, and helped her to the ranch house. Another hand realized what had happened and quickly rode out of the yard, whipping his horse frantically.

Rosa was trembling and had to hold onto the porch rail to keep from falling over as she knelt by the dog lying there covered with blood. She put her hands under his head and held it. She felt as if she were in a terrible nightmare—a puma attacking? The lion of the mountains did not attack people, or even dogs, unless it was cornered. What had happened? Why had the lion been so near the ranch, and why had it attacked her? Oh, poor sweet little doggy, little Job, you are hurt so bad, so bad!

E.J. came in fast on a lathered horse, took her into his arms and listened to what had happened. The men were standing around, jittery and looking frightened. Rosa didn't understand any of this and was feeling faint, but she slowly awoke to the sickening reality.

"Rosa, Liebchen, my dear, little Job-dog saved you, he saved your life. But, vell, you see, I vill have to put him down because dere sometimes are rabies outbreaks, und ve all know da puma vould not attack a human unless he vas rabid. Little Job has been slashed in many places, und it is all ve can do. Ve do not vant him in pain, do ve, Rosa? I am so sorry, but you are alright, und dat da main ting."

"Oh no, no, no." Then the realization really hit her. "Oh E.J., see the lion's claw or his tooth slashed my arm. See, it is not too much of a cut. See, it is not deep," and she held up her arm covered with blood. "Oh no, does this mean that *I*, oh no!" And she leaned against him to keep from falling.

"Oh my Got-in-Himmel, Rosa, no, Rosa, no! Any cut vould infect. Quick, Luca, get cole-oil, ve drench it und make bleed more." He picked her up in his arms and carried her to their cabin, barking orders at the men, "Jake, hitch up Blacky and Rufe to da good buggy. You be in charge here now. I take her to town. I hear dey have da injections, but not vone minute can ve lose."

He laid her on the bed, and he and Luca did what they could for the jagged cut. As Luca was binding it up, he said, "Luca, you will take over da kitchen, und Teresa," he put his hand on the small girl's shoulder, "Teresa, ve know dat you can look after da baby veddy vell, vill you do dat? You are good mit her und ve need you now more dan ever."

"Oh no, E.J.," Rosa cried out, "no, I can't leave the baby, I can't do that!"

He knelt by the bed and smoothed her hair. "Listen careful, Liebchen, you are infected by da cut; ve must get you to Tremonton now, right now. Dere are da injections dey give, und you must have dem. Dere is no minute to lose. Ve are dealing mit life now, your life. Injections must start in tree days I hear, und you must not nurse baby anymore. Now, Liebchen, she is year and half, she be fine vith Teresa; you know Teresa good mit her, she vill take good care of baby for us. Rosa dis only vay, you vill be sick, very sick; ve must leave now, right now."

She looked at his face. It was an ashen gray, and for the first time ever, she saw real fear in his eyes and cried out, "Oh no, don't let me die, please Lord, don't let me die! I can't die, my babies, my babies," and a sudden blackness engulfed her. She began slipping away, way down deep into a bottomless hole.

She fought through a dense dark blackness, tumbling down and down and down. It seemed she fell forever. Then there was a small beam of light. She fought with heavy arms and legs, fought and struggled with all her might, just kept struggling to get up to the small light above her. Suddenly there it was, she could almost touch it, and there, right there, was her mama, arms outstretched, reaching for her. "Oh Mama, Mama," she cried, "I can't die, my baby needs me, and Mama, I have another life in me, a new life. Oh Mama, help me, help me, Mama."

Mama's arms were holding her tenderly, and she began to feel a wonderful peace enfolding her. Mama was stroking her hair, and she could feel Mama's warm breast against her cheek. Her beloved Mama was telling her, "Oh, my little Rose-bud, hush now. It will be alright, Rosey, alright, yes, I am right here with your guardian angel. See, here she is, and we will be with you. You will be alright, you will be alright, my little Rosey. Shush, shush, hush now."

After a long time, Rosa opened her eyes, and the fright, the panic, was all gone. She was peaceful, her Mama was here, her guardian angel was here, she would be alright. Mama had told her she would be alright. She looked up at E.J. bending over her so concerned and frightened, stroking her forehead. "Oh my love," she whispered, "my husband, my love, I just saw Mama. She is watching over, she said I will be alright. Oh my dear, it was so peaceful and wonderful to feel her with me."

E.J. was shaking as he helped her to sit up. Rosa touched his white face and calmly told him, "Now, tell me what must be done. Yes, Teresa can look after Dorothea, and I know we will get to the doctor in time, but I must tell you now, dear, I, well, I had wanted to surprise you when I was sure, but E.J., I think I am again with child."

He cried out and held her against him, murmuring and moaning with his head against her neck. She reached up and wiped away the tears from his face, "Oh, Mr. Miller, Mr. E.J. Miller, you just quit that right now. I will be alright, dear. Mama said that she will be watching over us. Now, tell me what must be done."

She felt strength coming back as he helped her stand. She finished her cup of tea and started putting a few things in a small satchel very methodically. She would need a gown, a wrap, those moccasin slippers, an extra shirtwaist and skirt, underthings, a change of shirt for Mr. Miller. Oh, yes, she would need some extra pads for her breasts, as they would soon be dripping with too much milk. Oh, and her brush and hairpins and a clean bandage for the cut. She looked at her bandaged arm. Why, oh why didn't that claw miss me? But she had thrown up her arm to fend off the attack, so maybe it might have clawed her face instead. And if not for little Job leaping right up at the big cat, the sharp teeth and claws would have slashed her all over. She shivered and tried to put that out of her mind. Poor little Job, poor little doggy, so brave, so ferocious. He had defended her against the lunging lion with all his strength. She sobbed for Job, and the pain in her heart was unbearable— my poor sweet, little doggy!

In a very short time, E.J. was whipping the horses into a ground-eating trot. He knew these horses could sustain a pace like this for many hours at a time. He told her it would be long after dark before they reached the Culpepper's stop-over, so she should just try to sleep if she could. He had made her as comfortable as possible; she was huddled up on a big, soft buffalo robe with heavy quilts tucked in all around her. Where the going was smooth, E.J. held her against him, one big arm holding her tenderly. They didn't talk much. They had no need for talk, they must hurry, hurry, hurry!

She did drop off to sleep several times and wondered why she felt so tired. They stopped briefly a few times to blow the horses. One time he quickly used the little sterno camp stove and heated the hearty soup that Luca had packed. She ate willingly and felt so much better. "Oh E.J," she asked, "what about the cooking—do you think that Luca can feed the men?" He patted her shoulder, "I sent a man to get ol' Jonah, and in the meantime Luca said she would try. I told her the men would not mind beans and tortillas at all."

It was nearing midnight when they reached the Culpepper ranch, even though E.J. had pushed the horses almost to exhaustion. Rosa heard the dogs barking at their approach and again felt the heartbreak of losing her beloved Job; these barking dogs were little Job's family.

After E.J. had roused the house and carried Rosa into the ranch kitchen, he said he must tend his horses. Mrs. Culpepper quickly stoked up her stove and was a bundle of efficiency, heating the chicken soup left in the big iron pot. E.J. told her that he wanted Rosa to rest and sleep for about one hour. "Den ve must leave, ve must leave, vone hour, you vill see to her?"

"Yes, you know I will, E.J." And as he hurried out, Mr. Culpepper was saying, "E.J., we'll hitch up my two best harness horses, and they will get you to town lickety-split. She'll be OK, E.J, just OK, you'll see."

They traveled very fast the whole way, and just after dawn when the sun had warmed the land, E.J. stopped, checked the horses carefully, and helped Rosa prepare something hot. "Oh, I'm fine, Mr. Miller," she told him, "I'll do this." But she felt strange. This was not happening, this was just a terrible nightmare. She would wake any minute now, but she felt like all her movements were very slow, her limbs were heavy, and her mind was hazy-like.

As they traveled along at a very fast trot, she watched the country-side and remembered how it had looked that Christmas trip so many years ago. Now everything was in bloom. The cultivated fields, the cottonwoods, and every hillside were ablaze with a different color of yellow and green. Oh, it was so beautiful. They passed a few isolated ranches and then a few more. E.J. pulled up at one. "I heard dese folks have da telephone, Rosa, I'll see." In a moment he was back picking her up in his arms, "No, I vill carry. Come, da Missus here is making you hot soup. I must call doctor or hospital or someone to see vhat ve should do."

The big wooden phone with the crank was in the kitchen. Rosa could hear the near panic in her husband's voice as he explained what had happened. He turned to her quickly when he hung up. "Oh it is goot, Rosa. Dr. Drake does have serum, tank God, dey have serum, und he vill be ready to help soon as ve pull in."

In another couple of hours, E.J. was carrying her into the small two-story hospital in the town of Tremonton. "No, no, Rosa, I vil carry, I need to carry you."

There was a bustle of two lively nurses taking over as soon as she was put down on the hospital bed. The doctor started telling her what he would do as he prepared his injection. Oh, she was so tired, so tired. Her arms and legs were heavy, and there was a terrible pain now raging through her body. "Mama, Mama, I am so tired; Mama, where are you?"

Rosa could not recall anything that happened the next few weeks, only about waking sometimes with cold sweats and feeling again that pain raging all over her body. She would thrash about and cry out, but then Mama would come and pull her up out of that deep black hole again and again. Mama would hold her and soothe her, making those soothing sing-songs just like sister Belle did for her when she was a little bitty baby, and there was another presence there. Rosa knew that she was her own guardian angel, who had been with her as long as she could remember. And now she was here with Mama. Now the two of them were looking after Rosa. Then Mama would tell her, "Rosey, little Rosebud, you must be strong, you can do it, you are a tough little girl, you remember what a strong little homesteader you always were. You could do anything. You can fight, my little Rosey. The good Lord says you can do it, Rosey. We are here, little one, and I will always be with you. Hush now, shush, shush now."

Many times Mama came to her with her guardian angel, and they always made the feverish sweats and the awful pain go away for awhile. Sometimes she could feel E.J. sitting with her, holding her hand, whispering to her. She had a miscarriage and lost her baby, and she did not even know it until E.J. told her about it much later. Oh, another pain to bear. The baby was lost, her new little baby was lost forever. "Oh Mama, Mama, take good care of my little one for me, my little one I never got to hold. Oh Mama, I know you will look after him."

Then very, very slowly, day by day, she felt some strength flowing through her body. Most of the pain subsided, and she could finally sit up on her pillows. It was then that she realized that she would not die, that she was really going to be alright. Her mama had told her she would, and she really was. She was very surprised when E.J. told her that it had been a month and that he had just sent for Teresa and the baby, and they would be here soon.

One day a lovely bouquet of flowers was brought in with a note. "Dear Mrs. Miller," it read, "We all wish you a very speedy recovery."

It was signed, Mr. H. K. Wilie. Oh how nice, she thought, how very nice. Maybe he is not such a bad man after all. When she showed the note to E.J., he told her that Mr. Wilie had also insisted on paying all of the doctoring costs for them.

Then that very day, there was her own dear sweet baby, happy and healthy, gurgling at her, reaching for her. Oh, she held her so tight, and when she felt the fat little body against her breast, she cried and cried. Teresa was standing just inside the door, grinning from ear to ear. "Teresa," Rosa called, "Teresa, come here and let me hug you. How can I ever thank you for taking such wonderful care of little Dorothea?"

Now, she must hurry and get out of this bed, and soon she was actually walking around the room holding on to E.J.'s arm. It was then she realized how very sick she had been, because she had never felt this strange kind of weakness.

One afternoon E.J. said to her, "Now, Rosa Ellen, sit here und have your tea, I must talk mit you. Vel you see, I have decide, I, vel," he looked at her and then got up and started pacing back and forth. "I know, Liebchen, dat I vill not take you to live vay out on da ranch again, no, no listen, dere are reasons. I know it vas not fair to you, especially since you had to vork so hard, und I vill never have you vork like dat again, never. Und you could not even go to church on Sundays, und dere vere no vomen for you to visit vith, und I know dat vomen need dat, and vell, I have had da talk mit Mr. Wilie, und he seems to understand, Rosa. Aldough he offer me good raise if I stay, I say I cannot. I told him also dat I am not da farmer to learn how to raise da alfalfa seed; dat is vhat he needs now, is a foreman who knows about da growing of crops. Vell, after ve talk some more, und I made him see dat dis vas best for all, he vished us vell and gave us nice bonus besides."

"But, Mr. Miller, we—" she cried out, and he said, "No, Rosa, I have made up mind. Now listen, I have da plan. Sheriff Pete und I have been talking for long time; ve have been listening to all de news about da war. Vhile you vere ill, dere vas much fighting. It is as I feared, everyvone is fighting and dere are United States Army boys fighting und dying over dere right now, but you see dat I cannot pick up gun, go over dere und shoot my own broders, my own cousins, I cannot do dat, I cannot kill my own people." His voice sounded so pitiful, she jumped up and put her arms around him.

"Of course you cannot do that, but what can we do?" He sat her down again and regained his voice. "Pete says dey vill be needing every man who knows da machines to keep da trains moving, to help move da supplies for da war. Ve inquired, and dere is good chance dat I might get work in da Railroad Machine-shops in Pocatello, Idaho. Pete tinks dere vill be no questions ask about who I am, dey just need men. And Rosa, I had good training mit da machines; I vould make good machinist, I know. It vould be helping out. I must help out, don't you see? My Germany, my own broders have already killed da many people in dis terrible var. Dey make me feel guilty, like it my fault so many da people are dying; I must help in vay dat I can, I must—I must."

"Oh yes, my dear, of course, I understand, I do understand, dear, and whatever you decide will be alright. We will do whatever you think is best." She held his hands and tried to soothe him. Oh poor E.J., he is so torn. How terrible to think that his very own family is fighting and killing! Even killing American boys. She knew how much E.J. now loved America.

When he was calmer, he said to her, "Vell, Pete says dat he vill help find small house, maybe on some acres near Pocatello, vould you like dat?"

After he had gone to pick up Teresa and the baby, she lay back and realized that this was another turning point for them. She would miss the ranch, even the difficult times she would miss. But she was really glad—maybe they would have a home that was their very own. She could have time to be with her baby, and maybe there would be a garden spot and they could go to church; they could go to a social, they could visit with people. Oh, that sounded good, but the best thought of all was that they would not have to hide anymore.

In the next few days, E.J. and Pete made arrangements for Rosa and the baby and Teresa to stay in Pete's home for a few weeks while she was still recuperating. E.J. must spend a week out at the ranch with the new foreman. Then Pete and E.J. would make a trip to Pocatello together; there was a job to find, and they must find a place for them to live. E.J. and Pete would be gone awhile. They told her not to worry, she would be fine in Pete's house; he had a live-in housekeeper, and she sure was anxious to spoil Rosa and that baby. Rosa often thought about the friendship between Sheriff Pete and her E.J. It was such a very special bond, like a father for a son; perhaps Pete felt that way, and she knew that E.J. did.

While waiting for the men to return, Rosa spent her time taking some long walks and caring for the baby with Teresa, and she began to feel like her old self again. She was troubled about leaving the ranch and thought a lot about the Mexican children she had tried to teach. Then she had an idea. I will go to the Mercantile and purchase some slates and chalk and a few primers and have them sent out to the Wilie ranch. I am sure some of the older girls can help teach the young ones now. Oh, that will be fun, and I will send them out some other special treats, too. I have some money, and it will buy good-by gifts for all of them.

So she had a wonderful time picking out gifts and school things for everyone left at the ranch. She would write a long letter too, and one of the cowhands who can read could read it aloud to everyone. Oh, she thought, I wish I could see their little faces when these gifts are handed out. And I will send something pretty out to Mrs. Culpepper, too.

It was two weeks before Sheriff Pete came back. He told Rosa that E.J. was fine, he had the job, but would be delayed another week. She received one telegraph message from E.J. saying he would be there soon, everything was just fine, that he had a job, and found a house.

When he did arrive, Rosa was overjoyed with his news. Yes, he had a job, as an apprentice machinist to start, but a good chance to progress. And yes, he had found a house—well, not fancy, Rosa, but solid—and there are four acres that are fenced in, a couple of old apple trees, and a good garden spot. "The place is some overgrown," E.J. told her, "but dat easy taken care of, and dere are even da rose bushes at da front valkvay, Rosa. It vays out of town, but I can valk, or even get bike to ride to catch da trolley to da machine shops. I know you vill like it, Liebchen, and ve can leave as soon as you are able. Everyting of ours vas brought from da ranch. It stored over to da livery, so dere is not much for you to do but pack up da things you have here. Und Rosa, Teresa is going vith us; I ask her, and she is pleased to stay mit us; how about dat, liddle Liebchen?"

The next few days were hectic. Rosa was so excited and joyful that her strength seemed to be returning fast. She had put on a few pounds and started to look like her old self again. She was still very pale, but the happiness put the bloom back in her face.

They were on the train, and it seemed to Rosa to be a very slow one, she was so anxious. Then they were in a hired buggy, driving out of Pocatello. "Only few miles now," E.J. told them. They were passing many homes, mostly just modest, comfy looking houses. Oh, how good it is to be in a real neighborhood again, Rosa thought. She did not realize until now how much she had missed having neighbors.

They made a turn and started up a short lane. "Well, here it is, Leibchen, here is your veddy own home, Mrs. Miller," he said with pride.

She craned her neck around trying to look at everything. It was just as he had told her, a small house, sitting under a spreading tree with overgrown bushes around the small front porch. She could see that out back there were a couple of sheds and something that was probably a small barn. There was a wooden fence too, perhaps around a pasture plot.

As E.J. helped her down from the buggy, Rosa heard a high pitched whinny and another whinny. Oh, oh my, that was so familiar! She quickly ran around the back of the house and there, leaning over the fence, was her very own Kit-horse, neighing and pawing and tossing her pretty little head around.

Rosa just flew over that board fence, long skirts and all, and grabbed the little horse around the neck and hung there sobbing. Oh, her Kit-horse was here, that sweet, sweet husband, that wonderful husband! He had gone all the way to the Homestead and brought her Kit-horse home to her. Could any woman be so lucky and so blessed?

She clung to the horse. Kit's neck was silky and warm. Oh how precious. Now she had her E.J., she had her baby, and they had their very own home. But oh my, oh my, not in her wildest dreams had she ever imagined she would ever see her little mustang again, and here she was, here she was, right here, she could feel her, the soft living warmth of her. Oh, the joy was so sweet. "My dear Precious Lord, thank you, thank you, thank you for my guardian angels, thank you for looking after us, for keeping E.J. safe, and for helping me to be well again."

She looked up through her happy tears, and there were the three of them smiling at her. Teresa was peering over the fence, wiping her eyes, and there was her E.J., a huge grin on his face, standing there with his curly-headed little daughter in his arms. Oh, she was so much like her

178

daddy, and they were such a beautiful sight. And now they were safe at last, and all her loves were here, all together now.

Joy filled her heart, and she thought about this wonderful new beginning for all of them. Then, just for one fleeting moment, she was nine years old, and she was again driving in the wagon with Henry and Louisa and Mama. They were just topping the rise, looking down at that homely place they had come so far to see, their Homestead. She felt Mama's warm hand holding hers. It felt so loving, and she again heard Mama's sweet voice speaking softly, "Oh, praise-be to this day, for this day the Good Lord has set our feet upon this truly wonderful new, unventured path."

THE END

"Skinny Scotty"

Dear Reader,

I N WRITING THIS EPILOGUE for Mother Rosa's story, I found that I was rambling on more about feelings and emotions and sticking less to dates and facts. Well, that is just the way Mother told the stories of her life. So, if this epilogue is somewhat meandering, it is coming from the heart, and it must mean that I am more like Mother Rosa than I ever imagined. And that is a wonderful feeling.

In that year of 1919, the Miller family settled down quite comfortably in their little home on the outskirts of Pocatello, Idaho. They continued to live near Pocatello another twenty years.

E.J. was a valuable employee of the Union Pacific Railroad and advanced quickly to Master Mechanic and then to Master Tool and Dye Maker. Even during the long depression years E.J. was employed. Sometimes the work week was shortened, but at least the Union Pacific Railroad kept its men working so that they would be able to support their families. The Millers did not suffer as many other people did during those years.

Late in 1919 Rosa gave birth to a premature baby boy, and in those days premature babies did not survive. The doctor told Rosa, "The babe will not live through this night."

But Rosa, with her strong determination, refused to accept this. She asked sister Belle, who was there helping out, to bring her the baby and to warm some mineral oil. Rosa tenderly placed the very tiny body between her bare breasts and, softly, with tender fingertips, massaged and massaged the tiny boy, hour after hour, all through the night. And she kept this up for many days and nights. She must have literally breathed her own life into the child. She was determined that he would survive. He did live, and it was truly a miracle. He was so small that his bed was a cigar box, filled with cotton.

Little Pete Darrel Miller had some tough growing-up years, but at about the age of ten, he finally caught up and in time became a strong, healthy man. Rosa often said that little Petey was her brother Henry all over again. She called him Buddy, a nickname he carried all his life. And evidently Buddy had the same sweet disposition as her brother Henry. He had soft eyes and an innocent kindness in his heart. He was always a very gentle man.

In the year of 1926, I was born. June Elizabeth Miller was a healthy, chubby, pink baby with a completely bald head. Mother often said that I was the happiest and most good-natured of children, and of course I believed her.

By this time sister Dorothea was growing up, now ten years old. She was a beautiful girl with wavy auburn hair and her dad's green eyes. All my life, I envied my older sister for her good looks and vivacious personality. She was very much like Dad. In later life she was to become my best friend, and she was always there for me when I needed her.

My older brother Buddy was my God. I followed him and pestered him as soon as I could walk. He pampered me, was patient and always kind to me. He watched out for me at all times. This closeness continued all our lives. I often remarked, "Any girl would be truly blessed to have a big brother like my dear brother Bud."

During these early years, E.J. was studying very hard, and with Rosa's help, he proudly became a citizen of the United States. Dad would not speak of his own family and when asked, he would usually reply something like this: "Ve are da American now; ve are citizens of dis United States of America. For da family in Germany, I am veddy sorry, but I cannot tink of dat." When I asked him to teach me some of his

German language, he was adamant. "Nein, no, no, ve are American; ve speak da English only in dis land, dis America."

E.J. was a very, very strict father, but then he was of the old German school of discipline. Many, many times we children felt he was way too harsh with us, but his word was law. Oh, he did not have to ever punish any of us, because just a look from him was all that was needed to straighten us out immediately.

But we all worshiped him. He was funny and playful, and he comforted us with big bear-hugs on his comfortable lap. E.J. was a gifted musician. He just played instruments by ear; he could play the harmonica or the piano or the concertina with great gusto. He sang beautifully in that deep baritone. Oh yes, everyone loved big E.J., friends and family alike.

In the home, Dad's sometimes harsh discipline was always tempered with Mother's softness and kindnesses. She never disagreed with Dad's rulings, but somehow, when one of us was feeling put upon and really terrible, she always made everything alright again.

When I was ten in 1936, and we were still living in Pocatello, very unexpectedly a new baby boy was born. William Julius Miller was a healthy, robust boy with Dad's black curly hair, his dark complexion and hazel eyes. He was a very beautiful baby and grew into a very handsome man. He was an exact carbon copy of E.J. Dad was thoroughly delighted with this new son. He spent a lot of time with little Billy and did tend to spoil him. The rest of us, including Mother, were all amazed that Billy could get by with just about anything. Dad's discipline seemed to have disappeared completely where Billy was concerned. But thank goodness for Mother's calming influence and her quiet guidance with Billy when he was growing up.

We all often teased Bill later in life about being "the spoiled brat," but he overcame that and grew into a successful professional man. He is a dedicated geologist and naturalist. He became a Professor of Geology for schools in California. As a young man he was in the Navy. He married Geraldine Becker, and they had four children, Carla, Kurt, Julie and Jerod.

Dorothea married young and eventually lived in many different places around the world. She married Joseph St. Onge, an Officer in the Army Corps of Engineers. They had one child, Rhonda Lee.

Brother Pete was always a very industrious young man. During those depression years, he spent much time in the California Conservation Corps. Then after a stint in the Coast Guard during the second World War, he went to work for his first love, the railroad. He was very proud when he eventually worked his way up to become an engineer for the Union Pacific Railroad. He worked for several different railroads the rest of his years. He married Velma Ratliffe, and they had three children, Don, Janet and Joyce.

I guess I was the only one who did not quite conform. I left home at seventeen to be on my own, not to marry. I wore many hats. I thought I wanted to be a music teacher and studied and studied and did teach for a while. But to my disappointment, I did not have my dad's flare for music. Then during the war, I drove trucks for the Army in Fort Ord, California. Later I operated a gift shop at a mountain resort and was a packers' guide, riding horses and packing tourists into the back country of the High Sierras in California. Tiring of that, I became an airline stewardess and enjoyed the challenge of that for many years. At twenty-nine, I married Theodore Snyder, and we settled down in Los Angeles, eventually moving to Auburn, California. We had one son, Ted Miller Snyder, and he is still the joy of my life. Theodore and I divorced within eight years, and I continued working in Placer and Nevada Counties as a Real Estate Broker.

Son Ted was twenty-one and going off to college when I married a happy, charismatic man. H.P. "Mickey" Holden was a delight to every-one who met him. Ted and I were welcomed into Mickey's family with love. Now I was privileged to have two lovely adult daughters, Janis and Linda, and four beautiful granddaughters, Barbara, Melissa, Millie and Carrie. Ted and I were very happy to be part of this loving family. Mickey and Ted became like father and son. After Ted's college days, he married Patricia Bird, and they moved to the State of Washington, where Ted became a Fish and Wildlife Agent for the State. When Ted and Pat were expecting their first child, they asked us if they could change their name to Holden. Mickey said that this was the most wonderful gift he had ever received in his whole life. Ted and Pat Holden have two children, Aaron Park and Megan Rose Holden.

But many years earlier than all this, back in 1938 and 1939 while the family was still living in Idaho, E.J. developed a serious lung disorder. Several winters he was very ill with what Mother called a "pleurisy of the lung." The doctor finally told them that E.J. would have to get out of the machine shops of the railroad. He explained that the grit and dirt of the confined air inside the shops, along with the cold winters of Idaho, would kill him in a few years if he did not change his place of work.

Mother and Dad faced this with much concern, and they finally decided to move to California. Sister Dorothea was at that time living near Modesto, California, so they just packed up everything they owned onto a trailer, piled Billy and me into Dad's old Packard, and we headed south in 1939.

Work was scarce in those days, so Dad worked at many part-time jobs but finally, through great perseverance, landed a good job with the Spreckles Sugar Factory in Manteca, California. He was to be their Master Mechanic. He loved the work. He was not confined to a machine shop; he worked all over the huge plant, many times outside. He was a trusted employee for them for many, many years. The family had found a small farm near Manteca and settled comfortably into this new life in California.

Now that we had enough acreage, I could have a saddle horse. This had been a dream of mine for many years. From then on, I always owned horses. I guess Mother's love of a good saddle horse was passed down to me. Although I never had the chance to ride a single-footer, I did have a small bay from Nevada that was part mustang. Zipper had a very slow rolling lope that was not the same single-footed gait as her Kit-horse, but Mother said it looked oh so easy to ride. Zipper, though, was the best mountain trail-horse, as sure-footed as a goat on any rocky trail. I guess Zipper and I had the same love affair that Rosa had with her Kit-horse.

After high school in 1944, I left Manteca. By 1953, brother Billy also left home. He joined the Navy. Mother and Dad continued living on their small farm near Manteca.

When Dad finally retired from the Spreckles Sugar Factory, they moved up into the foothills near Auburn, California. They bought a small ranch and called it the "Hide-Away Ranch." They were very happy there and busy as they liked to be, raising cows, chickens, and rabbits, and cultivating a large garden. Rosa still loved to irrigate, and I remember, whenever I visited the ranch, seeing her out in the pasture in her overalls with a big hoe over her small shoulder, walking the gravity flow irrigation ditch. I knew it was her favorite chore.

Then there came a time when they decided they should sell the ranch and get a much smaller place. They moved to a cozy home and a small acreage nearer to Auburn. But they still had to have goats and chickens and rabbits, and a garden. Rosa became very active in her church, volunteering and helping out, and she and Dad also became very involved in the Senior Citizens organization of Placer County. They spent many happy hours dancing away an afternoon or working on community projects with friends at the Senior Center.

I think it was a contented, happy time for them. Undoubtedly though, their marriage was not all that much the proverbial bed of roses. There were plenty of ups and down, of course. Dad was a very stubborn dutchman, and he must be Lord and Master of his household. Mother Rosa always deferred to him in everything, and I know she did that because she could not stand any kind of confrontation; she always said nothing was worth arguing over. But we all knew that she was a very feisty lady who had her own opinions, so it was interesting to watch her diplomacy in sometimes turning Dad's thinking around when she thought it necessary. Somehow, she always let Dad think that he was having his way. It seemed she knew just how to handle his stubbornness and his volatile temper.

During this time, sister Dorothea suffered a great loss with the passing of her husband, Joseph. They were living in Texas at the time. Dad and I flew back there to be with Sis and her daughter Rhonda. It was the very first time that E.J. had ever been on an airplane; it was quite an experience for him. I can still see his eyes widening and see his white-knuckled grip on the armrest. "Vell," he said later, "dat vas someting! It sure feel like da bucking bronc."

Dad and I helped Sis and Rhonda move back to California to be near the family again. We were all glad they decided to do this, especially Mother.

On E.J.'s and Rosa's 50th Wedding Anniversary in 1964, all of us and all the grandchildren got together and threw them a wonderful 50th Wedding Anniversary Dinner and Dance. There were over 200 guests there to celebrate with them. Mother Rosa was certainly the "Belle of the Ball" and as beautiful as ever, now with silver hair. She was dressed in a pretty gown, the color of her snappy blue eyes. Dad was always such a handsome man, now large and a little portly, with a touch of white in his wavy black hair. I don't think I have ever seen him so proud. He was having the time of his life. His green eyes just beamed with happiness. When he took Rosa out on the dance floor for that first dance, there was not one dry eye in that hall.

Later, having a waltz with my Dad myself, I reminded him of the time when I was six and Dorothea was sixteen, and of all those evenings he spent with us, trying to teach our gangly legs how to waltz. He chuckled at that memory and said, "Und look at you now, Leibchen, a beau-ti-ful grown lady und valtzing like da angel. I did goot, I did goot, ya?" No one, absolutely no one, could waltz like my dad—he felt the music in every ounce of his being, and there were lots of ounces; he always weighed about 240 pounds. But he could waltz you around the room as if you were floating; he was just as light as a feather on his feet.

But there are always changes and challenges. Sooner or later there will be upheaval and pain in our lives. A few years later, brother Pete, our special Buddy, was diagnosed with a terminal illness and died soon after. All the family was devastated. Mother Rosa seemed to just wither away. Pete's family were pulled together by his wonderful wife Velma, and they slowly recovered. Eventually Mother, too, seemed to overcome some of her grief. Dad was very silent, but we all knew the pain of losing his first son was almost unbearable for him.

During the next few years all our lives resumed a fairly normal routine, with the family, including most of the grandchildren, living within driving distance of Mother and Dad.

But in August of 1969 another tragic upheaval changed everyone's life. A devastating fire took Mother and Dad's home. It was totally consumed. But that was the least of the tragedy.

It occurred one Sunday morning. As usual, Dad had driven Mother to her church and returned home. At this time a dear friend, an older man, was living with Mother and Dad in their home near Auburn. While Dad was outside watering the garden, he saw flames coming from the rear of their home. He immediately rushed into the house, which was by now almost fully ablaze. He rushed to the back bedroom and picked up his friend Claude, who had already succumbed to the smoke. He carried him out to safety. They were both burned, Dad most severely. Claude survived, but three days later Dad died from the smoke inhalation.

Mother was, of course, in deep shock for many, many months, and she kept saying over and over, "You know, I was not going to go to church that day; I had just about decided to stay home. But then a voice inside my head said, 'Go to church today. You must go to church today.' I know now that it was my guardian angel and my mama, they were keeping me safe again, because I would have been there in the house, too. But I guess the

186

angels could not save E.J. I guess that they and the Lord could not do that. I wonder why my guardian angels could not save E.J. too?"

After about six months, Rosa decided that she must get on with her life. "Just gonna pull myself up by the bootstraps," she told us. "I will be alright now." And she began making decisions, and she would not hear of any other way; she had decided. She wanted to have a mobile home moved onto their land and to make her home there alone. She was seventy-three at the time and physically very active, but we were all concerned about the pain and grief we knew she was trying to conquer with all this bravado. Nevertheless, we did as she wanted and made her comfortable in a mobile home. Her unbelievable strength at this tragic time in her life was amazing. She had often told us, as we were growing up, having to face some trial in our own lives, "Well dear, you will just have to put that ol' ramrod up your back and get on with your life." And that's just what she did, with no whining or self-pity.

After getting settled in, she insisted that she was going to drive again. She had not driven for some twenty years. She still had Dad's old Cadillac, and she learned how to wheel that big black beauty around like a pro. She passed her licensing and could now go to church on her own and get to her Senior meetings when she wished. With sister Dorothea living very close by, we stopped worrying so much about her. We were all just completely amazed at her gumption. Several years she was Senior Citizen of the year for Placer County and rode in the parade and was feted as a very special lady. She was very, very proud, indeed, of this accomplishment.

Some months after Dad died, the Carnegie Hero Foundation of the United States awarded Mr. Emil Julius Miller one of their prestigious Carnegie Hero Medals. Oh, what a proud day for Mother when she accepted his award. She told the audience of people there at the ceremony, "This wonderful medal is for a brave man who not only saved the life of his friend Claude, but a special man who, throughout his whole life, has been rescuing people from harm's way. Mr. E.J. would always just charge in without a moment's hesitation, without a thought of his own safety, when someone needed help. He was a hero many, many times in his life. Mr. Emil Julius Miller and I thank you very much for this great honor you have bestowed on him."

The Carnegie Hero Foundation people were gracious and helpful to Mother Rosa all the rest of her life. She received a monthly check from them to help with her living expenses. Each year a representative visited her personally. He became her very dear friend and usually prolonged his visit to spend a day with her. She corresponded with him and the Foundation often. He told me that her letters were a bright ray of sunshine to everyone in the Philadelphia office. They were passed around and enjoyed by all. I knew how outspoken she always was, and I often wondered what she was discussing in those letters. Later, when I wrote the letters as she dictated to me, I could tell why they were enjoyed. She always discussed any current topic, the state of the world, and especially the politics of the day. She had plenty to say about the leaders of our country. Many times she would relate some incident of her past to make a point—oh yes, they were delightful letters. They came from a very astute lady who had lived through the horse-and-buggy days to the age of the Moon landing. She had not been afraid of the changes; she seemed to enjoy the challenges of learning about something new and keeping up with everything going on around her.

But yet another challenge faced Rosa in her late eighties. Glaucoma took its toll, and she slowly became blind. She was well aware of what was coming and prepared herself. Her strength again seemed to come from that invisible, deep well inside her small body. "Skinny Scotty" could face anything, and she faced this final tragedy with poise and grace. She told me, "Well, sweetheart, this is just another step along a different path, but I will be alright." And yes, she was alright.

For the last five years of Mother's life she lived comfortably with brother Billy and his wonderful wife, Geraldine. Bill had retired early and built a home in Grass Valley, California, near where Dorothea and I then lived. Geraldine was born to be a nurse, I think. She is a wonderful cook and the kindest person I know. She took excellent care of Mother, and Rosa was very happy to be there with family.

During these years, I visited Mother often, and during our many long days of chatting, she would tell her stories. I am so glad that I had the foresight to tape-record most of our conversations. She loved to talk about her childhood and the growing up years on the Homestead, her big cowhand E.J., her marriage, the Utah ranch, and so much more. She told so many fascinating tales she made me feel as if I were there. These tapes eventually became *Skinny Scotty: The Adventurous Life of Rosa Ellen Scott.*

When she grew weaker and was mostly confined to her bed, she often would say to me. "Little Sweetheart, I wonder why the Good Lord is keeping me here so long. I am ready to go. I just don't understand what he is thinking about." And I would always answer, "Mom, I think it's because we all need you to stick around awhile: someone has to keep this family straightened out, you know, so the Good Lord must know that." Then we would launch into a discussion of one of the grandchildren's latest situations, and she would have me write a note to them about something she had been thinking on their behalf. She did have a way of coming right out and bluntly giving her advice to everyone, but sometimes she would discuss options and possibilities of a "different path," which was her favorite theme.

When I was growing up, I can remember her telling me many, many times. "Well, Little Sweetheart, it looks like you have two paths here. You are at that big Y in the road. Now tell me, what do you think will happen to you going down each path?" It took me many years to realize that her wisdom was always exactly right, but when I did go down the wrong path, which I often did, there were never any recriminations, just unconditional support in any path I chose. And that reminds me of Dad's favorite saying when I definitely made the wrong choice. In his brief, succinct manner he would always say, "Ah, Liebchen, somehow ve get too olt smart."

Mother knew when she was in her final time. She was peaceful and accepting. She was not in pain, the doctor said that she was just worn out—her age was catching up. So we all knew it was a matter of time, and we all did what we could to make her comfortable and occupied with visitors and the music she loved.

Then fate dealt another hand. Just a few weeks before Mother's death, my own personal world was torn asunder. With no warning, my own dear husband, Mickey, died. One second he was laughing, the next he was gone. He was a very, very special man in everyone's life, and especially in Mother's. She loved him dearly. The shock of this tragedy took a long time for me to comprehend, but immediately, I knew one fact; I would not, I could not, tell Mother of this terrible happening. I knew of the heartache this would cause her, and I knew what kind of pain she would be feeling for me and the family. I just could not burden her heart at this time with this new tragedy. I prayed for the guidance I needed to make this decision, and it was there. So, with the help of our wonderful family, I did not tell her. We kept it from her.

The first time I visited with Mother after this tragedy, she immediately knew something was wrong, and I thanked the Lord that she could not see my face. I tried to be calm and very matter of fact when I told her, "Oh, I'm alright, dear, just a little tired, been working too hard. But, Mom, you see, I do not want to lose you. I am so afraid of losing you, that, oh my, I guess that I am just not handling this very well, not very well at all." She held my hand and tried to assure me that is was alright, that it was her time. "Don't feel sad, sweetheart; promise me you won't feel sad."

But now my visits with her became the most distressing, the most unnerving and the most painful times in my life.

The very last time I was with her—just sitting, holding her hand— while we were listening to the hymns she loved. She said quietly to me, "My Little Sweetheart, I have had such a good, long life. There has been great love in my life. I have been a very lucky woman. Please don't grieve for me, Mein Liepchen, because you see, I am so happy to be traveling on now. I will be seeing Mama and that big handsome rascal, my E.J. Petey will be there and brother Henry too, so don't feel sad. Please don't feel sad for me, little Sweetheart. Don't you know that I will just be setting my feet upon a new and glorious unventured path."

Mother Rosa died quietly in her sleep that night. She was ninety-four and one-half years old. Later, in looking through her Bible, I found a yellowed paper with a short poem written in her hand. I recognized it as being the same poem she spoke of when she was grieving for her own dear Mama. It reads:

Tho I have had to leave you, whom I love,
To go along the silent way,
Grieve not, nor speak of me with tears,
But laugh and talk of me as if I were beside you,
For who knows that I shall be, oft times.

So, when you hear a word I used to say,
Or touch a thing I loved,
Let not your heart be sad, for I am happy here with Jesus,
And I am loving you,
Just as I always have.

June Elizabeth Miller Bussard

190